# Basic and Clinical Aspects of Neuroscience

Edited by E. Flückiger (Managing Editor),
E. E. Müller and M. O. Thorner

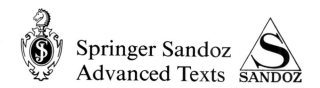

Springer Sandoz
Advanced Texts

# The Dopaminergic System

With Contributions by
B. Halász   K. Fuxe   L. F. Agnati   M. Kalia
M. Goldstein   K. Andersson   A. Härfstrand   B. Clark

With 23 Figures

Springer-Verlag   Berlin   Heidelberg   New York   Tokyo

Professor Dr. Edward Flückiger
Pharmazeutische Abteilung
Präklinische Forschung
Sandoz AG
CH-4002 Basel

Professor Dr. Eugenio E. Müller
Dipartimento di Farmacologia
Facolta' di Medicina e Chirurgia
Universita' degli Studi di Milano
Via Vanvitelli, 32
I-20129 Milano

Professor Dr. M. O. Thorner
Dept. of Internal Medicine
School of Medicine
University of Virginia
Charlottesville, Virginia 22908
USA

ISBN 3-540-13700-9 Springer-Verlag Berlin Heidelberg New York Tokyo
ISBN 0-387-13700-9 Springer-Verlag New York Heidelberg Berlin Tokyo

© Springer-Verlag Berlin Heidelberg 1985
Printed in Germany

The use of general descriptive names, trade names, trade marks, etc. in this publication, even if the former are not especially identified, is not to be taken as a sign that such names, as understood by the Trade Marks and Merchandise Marks Act, may accordingly be used freely by anyone.

Product Liability: The publisher can give no guarantee for information about drug dosage and application thereof contained in this book. In every individual case the respective user must check its accuracy by consulting other pharmaceutical literature.

Typesetting, printing and binding: Appl, Wemding
2121/3140-543210

# Preface

This new series of Advanced Texts on
*"Basic and Clinical Aspects of Neuroscience"* is a joint undertaking by Springer-Verlag and Sandoz Ltd. The series is designed to keep general practitioners and clinicians, as well as medical biologists and advanced students in medicine or biology, informed of the current state of knowledge in certain areas of neuroscience.

Each volume of the series is devoted to one topic and contains contributions by acknowledged authorities in their field. The authors are chosen not only for their expertise but also for their ability to convey their knowledge in a clear and straightforward manner, intelligible to the nonspecialist. Great emphasis is given to the illustrations, which are designed to enhance comprehension of the text.

The series is fortunate in having as editors Prof. E. E. Müller (Milan) and Prof. M. O. Thorner (Charlottesville), both for the planning of the program and for the contributions.

Basle, June 1985

E. Flückiger
Managing editor

# Table of Contents

# The Role of Dopamine in the Periphery

Barbara J. Clark

# Introduction to Neuroendocrinology

**Béla Halász**

*2nd Department of Anatomy, Semmelweis University Medical School, Tüzoltó utca 58, 1094 Budapest IX, Hungary*

In recent decades very spectacular progress has been made in the field of neuroendocrinology. We gained a vast amount of important new information which in essence confirmed and proved the original basic concepts of the discipline; however, it also led to a significant revision of our views about neuroendocrinology in general and about some of its special areas in particular. Forty years ago neuroendocrinology meant primarily neurosecretion as a peculiar phenomenon, the supraoptico- and paraventriculo-hypophyseal system producing vasopressin and oxytocin, and the neural control of the anterior pituitary gland. Nowadays the discipline covers much more. It deals with all interactions between hormones and nerve structures. There are an infinite number of such interactions, which exist at very different levels. Therefore, it is almost impossible to draw boundaries of the discipline and to give a more detailed definition.

As is often true in science, improvements in research tools have contributed greatly to the progress mentioned above. Refined techniques have been introduced for chemical characterization and synthesis of peptides. Immunological techniques, both radioimmunoassays and immunocytological methods, became available to measure minute quantities of hormones and neurohormones, and to identify and localize various peptidergic elements and other substances. New tract-tracing methods have been worked out for detailed analysis of neuronal connections. New pharmacologic research tools have also been developed.

Some of the main findings obtained in the last decades and greatly influencing the present picture of neuroendocrinology are briefly summarized on the following pages.

## Oxytocin- and Vasopressin-Producing Neurons

Until the 1970s oxytocin and vasopressin were thought of primarily as hormones of the posterior pituitary, produced by the neurons of the paraventricular and the supraoptic nucleus and released into the blood vessels of the neural lobe. This so-called paraventriculo- and supraopticohypophyseal tract was considered as a well-defined, distinct system producing the hormones responsible for contraction of the smooth muscles of the uterus and breast, and for antidiuresis.

The application of immunocytochemical and radioimmunoassay techniques to the study of the distribution of oxytocin and vasopressin has confirmed the original concept but, in addition, it has revealed the presence of both peptides throughout the central nervous system (Fig. 1). Vasopressin- and oxytocin-containing neurons which do not appear to project to the posterior pituitary have recently been identified both inside and outside the hypothalamus. Such vasopressin neurons were found, for example, in the hypothalamic suprachiasmatic nucleus, septal region, amygdala, and region of the locus ceruleus. Many oxytocin and some vasopressin neurons of the paraventricular nucleus give rise to projections to the brainstem and spinal cord (for references see [13]). There is an extensive network of vasopressin and oxytocin fibers distributed throughout the mammalian central nervous system. The areas containing such fibers range from autonomic centers or areas involved in nociception in the brainstem and spinal cord to forebrain limbic structures, and even to neocortex. Synapses in which the vasopressin- or oxytocin-containing nerve terminal is the presynaptic structure have been observed. Some of the projections of vasopressin or oxytocin neurons are already established.

The question arises: What are the functions of oxytocin and vasopressin in the central nervous system? There is experimental evidence that both hormones are involved in various brain functions. Behavioral effects of administered oxytocin and vasopressin have been observed, in particular their effects on memory and learning. There are also reports about other actions of these hormones (antipyretic, analgesic, etc.). Vasopressin may play a role in cardiovascular regulation through central pathways. Further, there is evidence that both vasopressin and oxytocin can alter the electrical activity of neurons or the catecholamine turnover in specific brain areas, or can influence cAMP production.

Thus, oxytocin and vasopressin, originally characterized as posterior pituitary hormones, appear to have an additional important role in influencing the activity of neurons through direct projections to these elements and hence may play an important part in a variety of central nervous system functions.

Basic and Clinical Aspects of Neuroscience
Springer-Sandoz Advanced Texts
© by Springer-Verlag Berlin · Heidelberg 1985

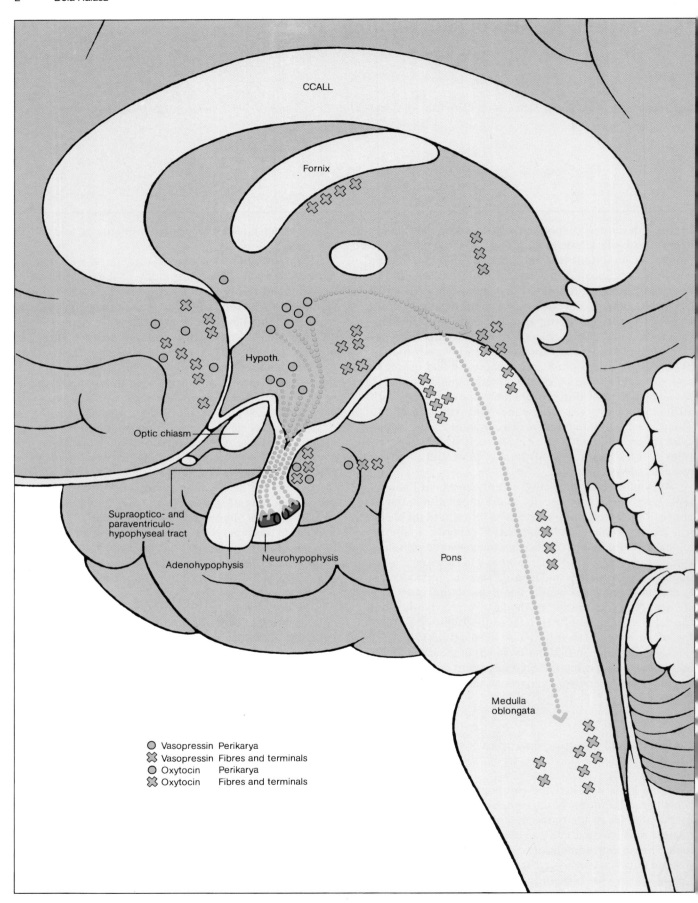

*Fig. 2.* Schematic illustration of the structural basis of the neurohumoral mechanism controlling the anterior pituitary

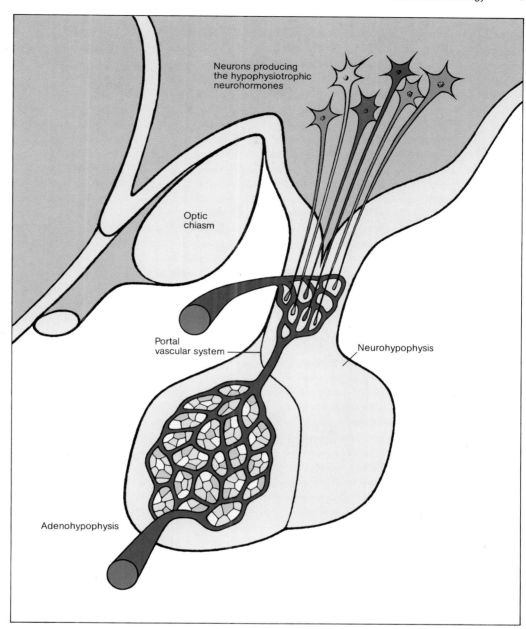

Neurons producing the hypophysiotrophic neurohormones

Optic chiasm

Portal vascular system

Neurohypophysis

Adenohypophysis

## Pituitary Trophic Hormone Releasing and Release Inhibiting Factors (Hormones)

In 1947 Green and Harris [6] formulated the concept that neural control of the anterior pituitary is exerted by a neurohumoral mechanism, i.e., the central nervous system synthesizes "hypophysiotrophic" substances which are released from the nerve terminals in the hypothalamic median eminence and pituitary stalk and they enter the hypo-

physeal portal vascular system by which they are carried to the cells of the adenohypophysis (Fig. 2). This hypothesis has been proved in the last two decades. Several peptides called have been isolated from the hypothalamus, chemically identified, and synthesized: a tripeptide [called thyrotropin releasing hormone (TRH)] causing release of the thyroid-stimulating hormone (TSH), a decapeptide [called luteinizing hormone releasing hormone (LHRH), gonadoliberin, or luliberin] with releasing activity for the luteinizing hormone (LH) and the follicle-stimulating hormone (FSH), a tetradecapeptide [named somatostatin, growth hormone inhibiting factor or somatotropin release inhibiting factor, (SRIF)] inhibiting the release of growth hormone and TSH (for references see [14]), and a peptide containing 41 amino acids [corticotropin releasing factor

⊲

*Fig. 1.* Distribution of vasopressin and oxytocin immunoreactive neuronal elements in the central nervous system. *CCALL, corpus callosum*

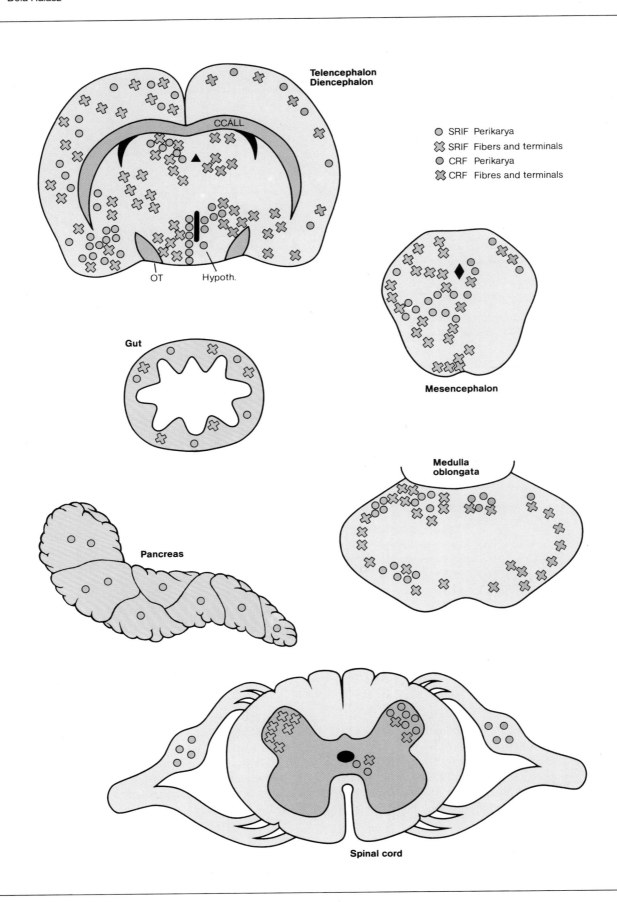

(CRF)] releasing corticotropin [15]. (Roger Guillemin, at San Diego, and Victor Andrew Schally, at New Orleans, received the Nobel Prize in 1977 for their major contributions to these discoveries.) It has been demonstrated that these peptides are present in the nerve terminals of the median eminence and proximal part of the pituitary stalk as well as in hypophyseal portal blood, confirming the idea of Green and Harris. It should be mentioned that most recently a growth hormone releasing factor which is presumably very similar, if not identical, to the growth hormone releasing factor occurring in the hypothalamus has been isolated from human pancreas tumor of acromegalic patients [7, 13 a].

Regarding the distribution of neurons producing these hypophysiotrophic hormones, a large amount of information has been obtained in recent years, some of which was in line with previous assumptions, while some was rather unexpected. Immunohistochemical studies revealed that such nerve cells projecting to the median eminence are distributed mainly in the medial preoptic, suprachiasmatic, and medial basal hypothalamic regions (see [14]). Within this area there are characteristic distributions of the neurons responsible for the production of the various neurohormones. But it also became evident that neurons containing one or the other of these compounds are widely distributed in the nervous system, present not only in the brain, but also in the spinal cord, the peripheral nervous system, and even in non-neural tissue such as the pancreas. Figure 3, showing the distribution of CRF- and SRIF-containing elements, illustrates this situation. Similarly, TRH is present in various regions of the brain and spinal cord, in the retina, pancreas and gastrointestinal tract, placenta, etc.

The wide distribution of these hypophysiotrophic neurohormones suggests that the functional significance of these substances is not limited to their action on the anterior pituitary, but that they may also function as neurotransmitters or neuromodulators influencing various functions of the nervous system or other functions outside the nervous system, such as insulin or glucagon release. Such an assumption is consistent with several recent findings. It has been observed, for example, that hypophysiotrophic neurohormone containing neurons are presynaptic structures in synaptic contact with other neurons. TRH has been shown to have a depressant action on cortical and hypothalamic neurons; in addition, it produces a number of behavioral alterations in rats such as increased spontaneous motor activity, suppression of feeding and drinking activity, inhibition of condition-avoidance behavior, and alteration of sleep patterns. There is also evidence that TRH inhibits gastric acid secretion, alters gastric motility, and can influence glucagon release (for references see [11]).

Thus, there is good reason to believe that, like oxytocin and vasopressin, the hypophysiotrophic substances are not only neurohormones acting on the anterior pituitary, but are also neurotransmitters or neuromodulators whereby they can influence various other structures and functions.

## Anterior Pituitary Hormones, Gastrointestinal Hormones, and Other Peptides in the Central Nervous System

Anterior pituitary hormone containing neurons have been discovered in the hypothalamus and in some other brain regions. Adrenocorticotropic hormone (ACTH) immunoreactive neurons, for example, were observed in the hypothalamic arcuate nucleus and in the nucleus tractus solitarius, prolactin nerve cells in the arcuate nucleus, and growth hormone in the amygdala. These hormones do not disappear from these regions after hypophysectomy, indicating that they are synthesized by neurons (for references see [13]). An increasing number of experimental data indicate that pituitary hormones, particularly ACTH, can act directly on various brain functions. De Wied and his associates [1] reported that ACTH delays extinction of food-motivated behavior in hungry rats and sexually motivated approach behavior. This favors the view that the action of the trophic hormones is not limited to the target endocrine glands or the mammary gland, or to stimulating growth, but that it may also directly influence different functions of the brain, in that the hormones act as neurotransmitters or neuromodulators. There is morphologic evidence that ACTH immunoreactive boutons form synaptic contacts with other neurons.

There are not only trophic hormones in the brain; gastrointestinal hormones such as cholecystokinin (CCK), vasoactive intestinal polypeptide (VIP), gastrin, and an increasing number of other peptides (opioid peptides, substance P, neurotensin, bombesin, angiotensin, etc.) were also found in the hypothalamus and in many other regions of the nervous system (for details see [13]). The hypothalamus is particularly rich in these substances. Besides influencing a number of nervous functions (producing marked antinociception, hypothermia, etc.), the majority of these compounds also affect anterior pituitary function, acting either via the hypophysiotrophic neurohormones or directly at the pituitary level [10].

Some of these peptides, such as opioid peptides, are also present in endocrine glands (in the gonads, the adrenal medulla). It has been observed that local injection of the opiate antagonist naloxone into the testis of immature rats stimulates spermiogenesis and enhances the rate of compensatory testicular hypertrophy following unilateral orchidectomy [4].

*Fig. 3 Distribution of somatostatin (**SRIF**) and corticotropin releasing factor (**CRF**) immunoreactive elements. **CCALL**, corpus callosum; **OT**, optic tract*

## Monoaminergic Systems

By means of the Falck-Hillarp fluorescence technique, the monoaminergic (dopaminergic, norepinephrinergic, epinephrinergic, serotoninergic) cell groups and their main projections have been identified. It was found that the majority of these neurons are situated in the lower brainstem, where various pathways arise and supply various regions of the nervous system including the hypothalamus with different monoaminergic fibers.

However, these studies have also revealed [2] that there are dopaminergic neurons in the ventral periventricular region of the hypothalamus projecting to one of the following regions: (a) the pars intermedia, (b) the posterior lobe of the pituitary, or (c) the surface zone of the median eminence and proximal part of the pituitary stalk, i.e., to the same region where the hypophysiotrophic neurohormones are released. The neurons projecting to the median eminence and the pituitary stalk form the tuberoinfundibular dopaminergic system. Their projection suggests that the dopamine released from these nerve terminals enters the hypophyseal portal vascular system and acts directly on the pituitary cells. This assumption has been experimentally proven; a number of studies have clearly shown that dopamine acting directly on the hypophysis inhibits the release of prolactin and represents one, if not the only, prolactin release inhibiting factor [16].

These data indicate that dopamine is not only a "classical" neurotransmitter but that it can also function as a neurohormone. This is just the opposite of what was discussed earlier. It appears that almost no distinction can be made between hormones, neurohormones, and neurotransmitters: the same substance may function in one place as hormone or neurohormone and in another as neurotransmitter or neuromodulator. This means, in other words, that the functional significance of such compounds is much broader than originally thought.

Besides basic information about the location of the various monoaminergic pathways, a significant amount of data has been accumulated [16] indicating that monoaminergic structures of the lower brainstem, primarily norepinephrinergic and serotoninergic elements acting through the hypophysiotrophic neurohormones, can alter (stimulate or inhibit) pituitary trophic functions. Norepinephrine, for example, stimulates LH release and inhibits ACTH release, and serotonin stimulates prolactin release. These observations suggest that the lower brainstem is involved in the control of the pituitary. There is evidence that the monoaminergic systems are influenced by, among others things, "feedback" action of steroids and other target organ secretions.

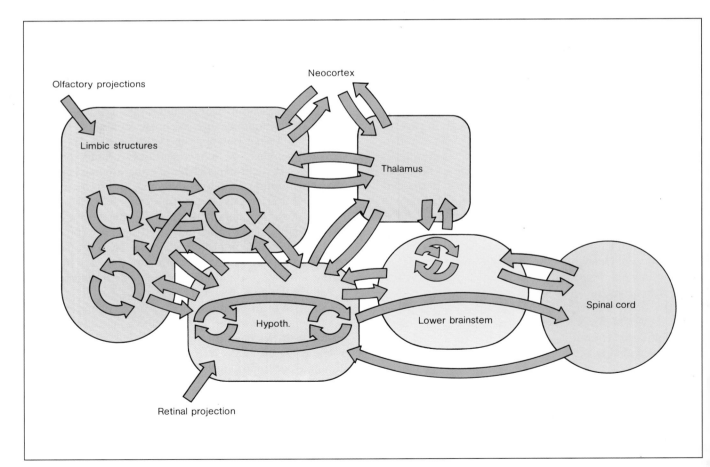

**Fig. 4.** *A simplified drawing of the neuronal circuits existing in and between various nervous structures involved in neuroendocrine functions*

## Structural Organization of the Nervous Elements Involved in the Control of the Pituitary

The general picture about the organization of the neural structures controlling the hypophysis has changed considerably in recent years. This is due partly to all the discoveries mentioned above, and partly to the application of new tract-tracing methods (using horseradish peroxidase, autoradiography, tritiated amino acids, the electron microscope to identify degenerated axon terminals, etc.), and to some quantitative analyses which provided a significant amount of new information.

It has emerged that, besides known connections, the hypothalamus is connected with the retina, the spinal cord, and many different regions of the brain. Almost all connections between hypothalamic and extrahypothalamic structures appear to be reciprocal.

Several data indicate that neuronal circuits exist at all levels of the control system, within cell groups or areas, and between cell groups within and outside the hypothalamus, suggesting an infinite number of interactions (Fig. 4).

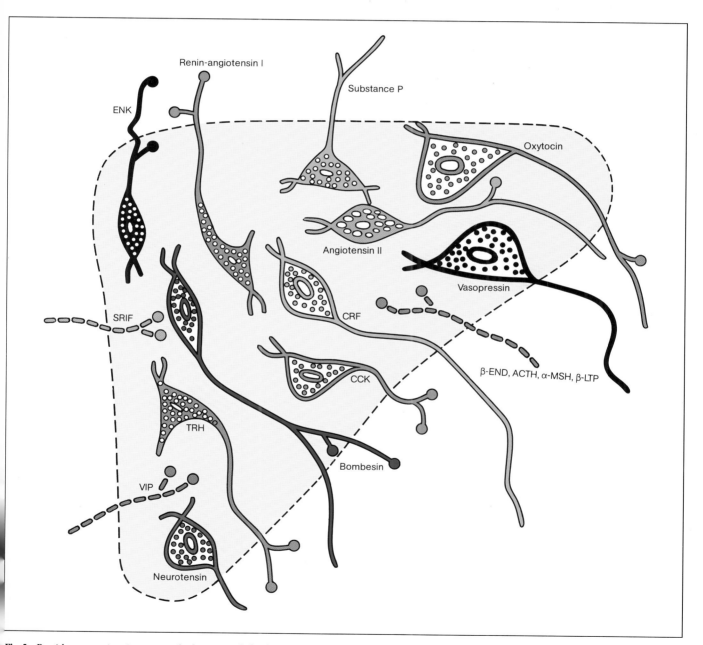

**Fig. 5.** *Peptides occurring in neuronal elements of the hypothalamic paraventricular nucleus.* **ACTH,** *adrenocorticotropin;* **α-MSH,** *alpha-melanocyte stimulating hormone;* **β-END,** *beta-endorphin;* **β-LTP,** *beta-lipotropin;* **CCK,** *cholecystokinin;* **CRF,** *corticotropin releasing factor;* **ENK,** *enkephalin;* **SRIF,** *somatostatin;* **TRH,** *thyrotropin releasing hormone;* **VIP,** *vasoactive intestinal polypeptide*

There is also evidence that the neurons producing the neurohormones send axon collaterals to adjacent neurons or to other regions, indicating that even the neurohormone-secreting nerve cells do not represent a single (humoral) output channel, but can at the same time also influence other neurons (for details see [8]).

As mentioned, an extremely large number of peptides and other compounds are evident in the central nervous system, particularly in the hypothalamus, which presumably participate in communication by neurons. One cell group or nucleus may contain several of these substances (Fig. 5).

There are usually about 1000 or more synapses per neuron in the hypothalamus, indicating the large number of influences a neuron might be subjected to.

When discussing structural features, mention should be made about sex differences in structure and about the perinatal action of sex hormones in the determination of sex differences in structure and function of the central nervous system. Gorski and his associates [5] found that there is a cell group in the medial preoptic area which is larger in the male than in the female rat (it has been named the sexually dimorphic nucleus). Further, it has been reported that estrogens can stimulate synaptogenesis [9].

## Peripheral Innervation of the Endocrine Glands

Until quite recently it was generally assumed that the function of the gonads or the adrenal cortex is primarily controlled by the hypothalamus-anterior pituitary system, and that the peripheral control mechanisms operating at the level of the gland play only an insignificant role in the control. The information accumulated in recent years does not support such a view, but indicates the importance of the "periphery." The local effect of the opiate antagonist naloxone on the testis (mentioned above) is in line with this new assumption. There are also several other findings which support it. Local pharmacologic denervation of one of the ovaries with 6-hydroxydopamine results in a significant weight increase of the nontreated organ, with no change in the weight of the treated ovary. In unilaterally ovariectomized rats, local treatment of the remaining ovary with 6-hydroxydopamine prevents the development of the compensatory ovarian growth. Hemitransection of the spinal cord on the side contralateral to the removed ovary blocks the compensatory hypertrophy after unilateral ovariectomy [3]. Abdominal vagotomy delays the onset of puberty and inhibits ovarian function in the female rat [12]. All these observations favor the idea that there are neural connections, both afferent and efferent, between the hypothalamus and the gonads which may be involved in the control of these endocrine glands.

*In summary,* it is impossible to draw boundaries between the nervous system and the endocrine system, and between nerve structures involved in neuroendocrine

mechanisms and the rest of the brain. The neurohormones, having classical roles as hypothalamic releasing or inhibiting hormones regulating the anterior pituitary or being delivered into the blood stream by nerve terminals in the neural lobe, are neurotransmitter candidates. The opposite is also true. A "classical" neurotransmitter can also function as a neurohormone. Dopamine, which is dealt with in this first volume of *Basic and Clinical Aspects of Neuroscience,* is a good example of a substance working both as a neurotransmitter and as a neurohormone, and having very important clinical implications both in neurologic diseases and in endocrine dysfunctions. Further, there is an increasingly long list of peptides (including several hormones) and other substances synthesized by both the nervous system and the peripheral organs (including endocrine glands) that appear to possess neurotransmitter capability. It is also clear that hormones exert very significant multiple feedback actions on the nervous system. The nervous structures involved in the neuroendocrine mechanisms are manifold interrelated with each other and with the rest of the brain.

All these findings indicate that the nervous and endocrine systems function as a single great integrative system in the organism.

## References

1. De Wied D (1983) Neuropeptides and adaptive behavior. In: Endrőczi E, de Wied D, Angelucci L, Scapagnini U (eds) Developments in neuroscience, vol 16. Elsevier Biomedical, Amsterdam, pp 3–21
2. Fuxe, K, Hökfelt T (1969) Catecholamines in the hypothalamus and the pituitary gland. In: Ganong WF, Martini L (eds) Frontiers in neuroendocrinology. Oxford University Press, New York, pp 47–96
3. Gerendai I, Halász B (1981) Participation of a pure neuronal mechanism in the control of gonadal functions. Andrologia 13: 275–282
4. Gerendai I, Nemeskéri Á, Csernus V (1983) Naloxone has a local effect on the testis of immature rats. Andrologia 15: 398–403
5. Gorski RA, Gordon JH, Shryne JE, Southam AM (1978) Evidence for a morphological sex difference with the medial preoptic area of the brain. Brain Res 148: 333–346
6. Green JD, Harris GW (1947) The neurovascular link between the neurohypophysis and adenohypophysis. J Endocrinol 5: 136–146
7. Guillemin R, Brazeau P, Bohlen P, Esch F, Ling N, Wehrenberg WB (1982) Growth hormone-releasing factor from a human pancreatic tumor that caused acromegaly. Science 218: 585–587
8. Halász B, Réthelyi M, Kiss J, Nagy L (1980) Intra- and extrahypothalamic neuronal circuits in the control of anterior pituitary function. In: Cunning JA, Funder JW, Mendelsohn FAO (eds) Endocrinology. Australian Academy of Science, Canberra, pp 630–633
9. Matsumoto A, Arai Y (1976) Effect of estrogen on early postnatal development of synaptic formation in the hypothalamic arcuate nucleus of female rats. Neurosci Lett 2: 79–82
10. McCann SM (1982) The role of brain peptides in the control of anterior pituitary hormone secretion. In: Müller EE, MacLeod RM (eds) Neuroendocrine perspectives. Elsevier, Amsterdam, pp 1–22
11. Morley JE (1979) Extrahypothalamic thyrotropin releasing hormone (TRH) – its distribution and its functions. Life Sci 25: 1539–1550

12. Ojeda SR, White SS, Aguade LI, Advis JP, Andersen JM (1983) Abdominal vagotomy delays the onset of puberty and inhibits ovarian function in the female rat. Neuroendocrinology 36: 261–267

13. Palkovits M (1982) Recent data on neuropeptide mapping in the central nervous system. In: McKerns KW, Pantic V (eds) Hormonally active brain peptides, structure and function. Plenum, New York, pp 279–306

13a. Rivier J, Spiess J, Thorner MO, Vale W (1982) Characterization of a growth hormone-releasing factor from a human pancreatic islet tumor. Nature 300: 276–278

14. Sétáló G, Flerkó B, Arimura A, Schally AV (1978) Brain cells as producers of releasing and inhibiting hormones. Int Rev Cytol [Suppl] 7: 1–52

15. Vale W, Spiess J, Rivier C, Rivier J (1981) Characterization of a 41-residue ovine hypothalamic peptide that stimulates secretion of corticotropin and $\beta$-endorphin. Science 213: 1394–1397

16. Weiner RI, Ganong WF (1978) Role of brain monoamines and histamine in regulation of anterior pituitary secretion. Physiol Rev 58: 905–976

# Dopaminergic Systems in the Brain and Pituitary*

Kjell Fuxe, Luigi F. Agnati, Madhu Kalia, Menek Goldstein, Kurt Andersson, and Anders Härfstrand

Department of Histology, Karolinska Institutet, Stockholm, Sweden; Department of Human Physiology, University of Modena, Modena, Italy; Department of Pharmacology, Thomas Jefferson University, Philadelphia, USA and New York University Medical Center, New York, USA

## Abbreviations in Figures

| | |
|---|---|
| Acb | accumbens nucleus |
| AOP | anterior olfactory nucleus, posterior part |
| APit | anterior lobe of the pituitary |
| CPu | caudate putamen (striatum) |
| DM | dorsomedial hypothalamic nucleus |
| DSS | diencephalospinal DA system |
| FrPaM | frontoparietal cortex, motor area |
| GP | globus pallidus |
| ic | internal capsule |
| IPit | intermediate lobe of the pituitary |
| LHb | lateral habenular nucleus |
| LS | lateral septal nucleus |
| mfb | medial forebrain bundle |
| SNC | substantia nigra, compact part |
| SNR | substantia nigra, reticular part |
| STh | subthalamic nucleus |
| Tu | olfactory tubercle |
| VMH | ventromedial hypothalamic nucleus |
| VTA | ventral tegmental area (Tsai) |

It is now 20 years since Swedish scientists described the existence of the nigrostriatal, mesolimbic, and tuberoinfundibular dopaminergic (DA) neurons in the rat brain [4, 8, 13, 17, 24, 50]. Since then new types of DA neuronal systems in the brain have been mapped out and the existence of peptide comodulators in certain subpopulations of DA neuronal systems has been described [27–29]. Of considerable importance in the mapping of new types of DA systems (Tables 1, 2, and 3) has been the development of new sensitive fluorescence methods for the demonstration of DA, based on the same histochemical principles as the classical formaldehyde method, and the biochemical purification of tyrosine hydroxylase (TH) [41] has made it possible to use TH immunocytochemistry in the mapping of the central DA neuronal systems [23, 25, 27, 33, 34, 38]. It is important to emphasize that although the various DA neuronal systems have been described mainly in the rat brain, they also exist in the primate and human brains, although the details of their anatomy remain to be completely worked out [43]. In this review we present a brief description of the morphofunctional characterization of the various DA neuronal systems in the central nervous system (CNS), as well as their relationships to the pathophysiology of Parkinson's disease, schizophrenia, and various neuroendocrine disorders [24]. In principle, the central DA neurons can be divided into ascending, descending, and local neuron systems.

## Ascending DA Neuron Systems

### Morphology of the Nigrostriatal DA System (New Nomenclature: Dorsal Component of the Mesostriatal DA System)

The origin of the dorsal component of the mesostriatal pathway is in the substantia nigra, especially in the zona compacta (group A9). In man, the multipolar DA neurons are deeply pigmented and their dendritic tree arborizes in the ventrally located zona reticulata (Fig. 1). A dendritic release of DA regulates the activity in afferent terminals to the zona reticulata arising in the basal ganglia. The DA-containing axon bundles of the nigral DA cells in turn project to the nucleus caudatus and putamen via the medial forebrain bundle and subsequently the internal capsule (Fig. 2). The entire nucleus caudatus and putamen are densely innervated by these nigral DA axons, and collaterals of the nigral DA axons also sparsely innervate the nucleus subthalamicus and the globus pallidus. In the basal ganglia, two types of DA nerve terminal populations are found. The vast majority form a diffuse, dense innervation and the others form distinct DA islands (also called striosomes, or subcallosal striae) in the nucleus caudatus. There is a precise mediolateral and anterior-posterior topography within the nigrostriatal DA system. The nigrostriatal DA system is mainly ipsilateral with a small number of crossed DA fibers. This pattern is typical for all the ascending mesotelencephalic DA pathways.

A minor component of the striatal DA innervation originates in the A8 DA cell group (caudal extension of

* This work has been supported by grant 04X-715 from the Swedish Medical Research Council, grants HL 30991 and MH 25504 from the USPHS, and a grant from the Knut and Alice Wallenberg Foundation.

**Table 1.** *Ascending dopamine neurons*

| System | | | Origin | Pathway | Innervation area |
|---|---|---|---|---|---|
| 1. Nigrostriatal (Dorsal part of mesostriatal pathway) | | – Major | Substantia nigra (A9) | MFB IC | Nucleus caudatus putamen, globus palladus, subthalamic nucleus |
| | | – Minor | Retrorubral reticular nucleus (AB) | MFB IC | Ventral putamen |
| | | – Minor | Ventral tegmental area (A10) (lateral) | MFB IC | Anteromedial part of nucleus caudatus putamen |
| 2. Mesolimbic (Ventral part of mesostriatal pathway) | | – Major | Ventral tegmental area (A10) | MFB | Nucleus accumbens, tuberculum olfactorium, nucleus interstitialis striae terminalis |
| | | – Minor | Substantia nigra (A9) (medial) | MFB | Nucleus accumbens |
| 3. Mesolimbic-cortical | | – Major | A10 | MFB | Septum, hippocampus, amygdala, entorhinal cortex (ventral), anteromedial frontal cortex (pregenual, supragenual), perirhinal cortex |
| | | – Minor | A9 | MFB | Piriform cortex (medial A9), hippocampus, amygdala (medial A9), frontal suprarhinal cortex |
| 4. Mesothalamic | | – Major | Interfasicular nucleus | Fasciculus retroflexus | Medial habenular (medial part) |
| | | – Major | Medial paranigral nucleus (A10) | Fasciculus retroflexus | Lateral habenular (medial part) |

MFB, medial forebrain bundle
IC, internal capsules

**Table 2.** *Descending dopamine neurons*

| System | | Origin | Pathway | Innervation area |
|---|---|---|---|---|
| 1. Diencephalospinal | – Major | Periventricular gray (A11) of caudal hypothalamus and thalamus | Dorsal longitudinal fasiculus of Schutz and dorsolateral funiculus of spinal cord | Rexed laminae II–V (lateral) of cervical, thoracic, lumbar and sacral spinal cord and IMLC of thoracic cord |
| 2. Mesoceruleo (mesopontine) | – Major | A9, A10 | Probably central tegmental tract | Locus ceruleus lateral parabrachial nucleus |
| 3. Mesocerebello | – Major | A8, A9, A10 | Unknown | Purkinje cell layer of cerebellum |
| 4. Vagal preganglionic | – Major | Medial, caudal dmnX (caudal and medial part of A2) | Vagus nerve | Thoracic viscera |

IMLC, intermediolateral column

group A9), located dorsolateral and caudal to group A9, and partly within the retrorubral nucleus. The A8 group innervates the ventral putamen (Fig. 2).

### Nigral Afferents

The main transmitter-identified afferent inputs to the substantia nigra consist of the striatonigral neuron systems containing substance P or dynorphine, and the striatopallidonigral GABAergic pathways, all of which give rise to a rich innervation of the substantia nigra and especially of the zona reticulata, where the DA dendrites ramify [see 33]. These different types of striatonigral pathways form im-

portant outflow systems from the basal ganglia. In addition, the DA cell bodies in the substantia nigra are richly innervated by neurotensin immunoreactive nerve terminals and possess neurotensin receptors.

### Biochemical Heterogeneity of Nigral DA Cell Bodies

Within the substantia nigra (mainly medial and lateral part) a subpopulation of DA neuronal perikarya have been demonstrated to contain cholecystokinin (CCK)-like immunoreactivity. These CCK-like peptides seem to have some functional significance in the substantia nigra itself, since very few CCK-immunoreactive DA nerve terminals exist in the nucleus caudatus putamen.

**Table 3.** *Local neurons of the midbrain hypothalamus and preoptic area*

| System | | Origin | Innervation area |
|---|---|---|---|
| 1. Mesencephalic periaque-ductal | – Major | Periaqueductal dopamine cells (A11a) | Local and periventricular fibers |
| 2. Periventricular hypotha-lamic and preoptic | – Major | i. Periventricular hypothalamus (ventral part belonging to A12, outermost part belonging to A14) ii. Periventricular-preoptic area (A14) iii. A11 | Local and periventricular fibers, medial and midline thalamus and septum (mainly A11) |
| 3. Incerto hypothalamic | – Major | Medial zona incerta (A13) | Local; dorsal and anterior hypothalamus and medial preoptic area |
| 4. Tubero infundibular | – Major | Arcuate and periarcuate nucleus (A12) | External layer of medial eminence and infundibular stalk |
| 5. Tubero hypophyseal | – Major | (Anterior A12) | Intermediate lobe (entire extent) and neural lobe of hypophysis |
| 6. Other types of hypothalamic DA cell groups | – Major | (Paraventricular hypothalamic nucleus and dorsomedial hypothalamic nuclei, supramammillary area, premammillary area, and border zone between medial and lateral hypothalamus, ventral to the fornix, area along ventral surface | Local interneurons |

## Morphology of the Mesolimbic DA System (New Nomenclature: Ventral Component of the Mesostriatal DA System)

The ventral component of the mesostriatal DA pathway originates mainly in the ventral tegmental area and the medial part of the substantia nigra and innervates the nucleus accumbens, tuberculum olfactorium, and nucleus interstitials striae terminalis pars dorsalis (Fig. 3). The pathway reaches the innervation area mainly via the medial forebrain bundle.

The dorsal striatum is innervated by sensory and motor neocortex, whereas the ventral striatum is innervated by limbic cortical regions such as the piriform cortex, amygdaloid cortex, and the entorhinal cortex [see 33, 34]. The ventral striatum sends its efferents mainly to the ventral pallidum (ventral part of globus pallidus), which sends fibers to the dorsomedial thalamic nucleus, which projects into the prefrontal cortex. This efferent outflow most probably operates via, inter alia, GABAergic and enkephalinergic mechanisms. The globus pallidus projects to the ventrolateral and ventroanterior nuclei of the thalamus, which in turn project into the motor cortex.

### Ventral Tegmental Afferents

Cells in the ventral striatum and in the hypothalamus and preoptic area project into the ventral tegmental area (group A 10). They seem to operate at least in part via release of GABA as a neurotransmitter. In addition, neurotensin and noradrenergic terminals in the A 10 area are probably active in the regulation of the DA cell activity of this region.

### Discrete DA Projections to Ventral Striatum

Although there are probably subtypes of DA projections in the innervation of nucleus accumbens, tuberculum olfactorium, and nucleus interstitialis striae terminalis dorsal part, there are strong indications that there is also collateralization in the organization of the ascending ventral tegmental DA neurons. Tuberculum olfactorium seems mainly to be innervated by axons originating in the lateral part of group A 10, while the medial part of group A 9 contributes to a minor extent to the innervation of the nucleus accumbens. The mesoaccumbens DA projection shows a distinct mediolateral topography.

### Biochemical Heterogeneity of the Mesolimbic DA Neurons

Especially the lateral component of the A 10 group, located mainly in the nucleus parabrachialis pigmentosus, contains CCK-like immunoreactivity. In addition, a subpopulation of DA nerve terminals which store CCK-like immunoreactivity has been discovered in the caudal part of the nucleus accumbens and tuberculum olfactorium. These DA nerve terminal networks probably originate from the DA-CCK cell bodies of the A 10 group [29]. The CCK-DA immunoreactive nerve terminals in the ventral striatum have previously been identified as being of the dotted type with a low DA turnover. It must be emphasized that the CCK-DA nerve terminals of the ventral striatum represent a small proportion of its rich DA networks, which are mainly of the diffuse type.

Neurotensin-like immunoreactivity has also been shown to exist in another subgroup of A 10 DA nerve cell

*Fig. 1A.* *Low-power bright field photomicrograph of the ventral mesencephalon showing the caudal and lateral extension of the substantia nigra into the mesencephalic reticular formation, an area filled with TH-immunoreactive neurons, dendrites, and axons (group A 8). Dorsal (**D**) is at the **top** and medial (**M**) is to the **left** of the figure. **B.** High-power photomicrograph of the caudal extension of the substantia nigra shown in **A**. Note the dense dendritic arborization in this region (zona reticulata). **C.** Low-power photomicrograph of the medial forebrain bundle (**MFB**) containing TH-immunoreactive (dopaminergic) axon bundles coursing laterally (to the left) into the internal capsule. Bar = 200 μm*

bodies, indicating that in addition to topological differences there are also significant biochemical heterogeneities in the group A 10 area.

## Morphology of the Mesolimbocortical DA System

The mesolimbocortical DA system also originates primarily from the ventral tegmental area (A 10 cell group). Minor projections of this DA system also arise from the substantia nigra (group A 9). The DA fibers ascend in the medial forebrain bundle and innervate the septum (mainly lateral septal nucleus), many limbic cortical regions, such as the amygdaloid cortex and the hippocampus, and the supragenual and pregenual anteromedial cortex (prefrontal cortex) (Fig. 4). Some DA fibers also extend into the anterior olfactory nuclei and into the olfactory bulb. Although at

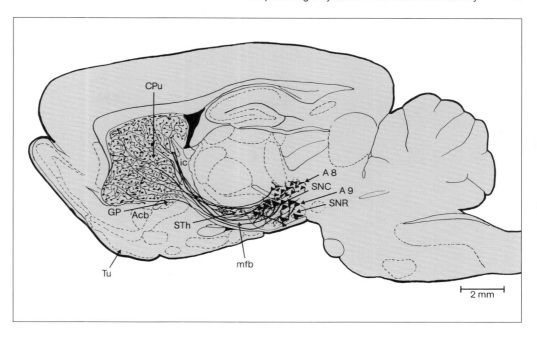

**Fig. 2.** *Drawing of a sagittal section of a rat brain modified from the atlas by Paxinos and Watson (1982) showing the* <u>*nigrostriatal DA pathway*</u> *at a level 2.4 mm lateral to the midline [42]. Neuronal perikarya are represented as **triangles**, nerve axons as **solid lines**, and **dots** represent nerve terminals and en passant boutons. Notice the arborization of dendrites of nigral neurons of the pars compacta in the pars reticulata. Axon collaterals can be seen in the subthalamic nucleus (**STh**) and globus pallidus (**GP**) before the dense terminal arborization in the caudate nucleus putamen (**CPu**)*

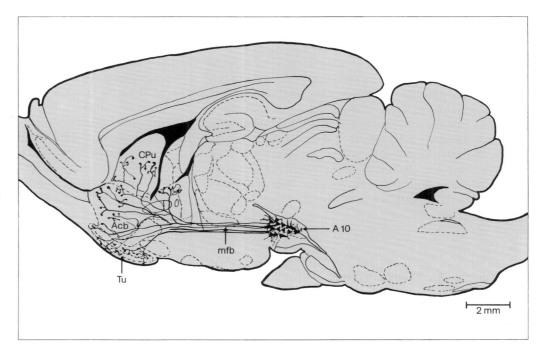

**Fig. 3.** *Drawing of a sagittal section of a rat brain modified from the atlas by Paxinos and Watson (1982) showing the* <u>*mesolimbic DA pathway*</u> *at a level 1.4 mm lateral to the midline [42]. Neuronal perikarya are represented as **triangles**, nerve axons as **solid lines**, and **dots** represent nerve terminals and en passant boutons. Notice the arborization of dendrites of the A10 cell group in the ventral tegmental area. Dense terminal arborization can be seen mainly in the nucleus accumbens (**Acb**) and tuberculum-olfactorium (**Tu**), but also in the medial caudata putamen (**CPu**) and islands of Calleja (**ICj**)*

the present time there is convincing evidence that there is a certain degree of collateralization in the mesolimbic and mesolimbocortical DA neuron system, it seems that the ventral tegmental area as well as the adjacent substantia nigra is built up of discrete DA cell body populations projecting into separate DA nerve terminal fields, where they form dense DA networks. Therefore, there is a considerable degree of topological heterogeneity within the ascending DA neuron systems. It is evident from the distribution of the cortical DA nerve terminal networks that, at least in the rat brain, they are mainly distributed to the limbic cor-

tex, with the exception of the frontal cortex. Thus, the neocortical regions are dominated by noradrenaline and 5-hydroxytryptamine innervation.

## Morphology of the Mesothalamic DA Systems

The mesothalamic DA pathway originates in the ventral tegmental area (A10 group). The DA axons reach the habenula via the fasciculus retroflexus and arborize mainly in the medial parts of the lateral and medial habenula

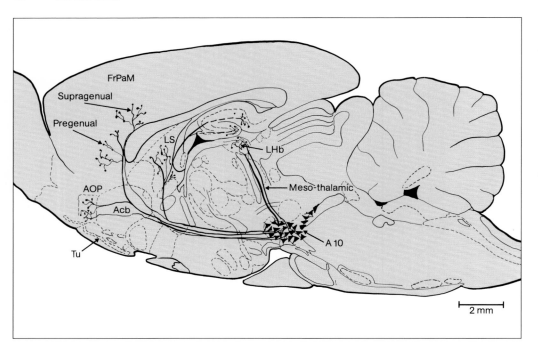

**Fig. 4.** Drawing of a sagittal section of a rat brain modified from the atlas of Paxinos and Watson (1982) showing the medial component of the mesolimbocortical DA pathway at a level 0.9 mm lateral to the midline [42]. Neuronal perikarya are represented as **triangles**, nerve axons as **solid lines**, and **dots** represent nerve terminals and en passant boutons. Axons arising from the A10 cell group also give rise to the mesothalamic pathway that innervates the medial and lateral habenula. The mesoseptal pathway to the lateral septal nucleus is illustrated, as well as the terminal arborizations in the posterior subnucleus of the anterior olfactory nucleus (**AOP**) and in the supragenual and pregenual regions of the prefrontal motor cortex (**FrPaM**)

(Fig. 4) [44]. The lateral habenula is an important relay station for circuits in the extrapyramidal system. For example, both the dorsal and the ventral pallidum send afferents into the lateral habenula, and the lateral habenula in turn projects to the reticular formation of the midbrain and into the substantia nigra. Nerve fibers of the dorsal and ventral striatum therefore converge in the lateral habenula. It has also been discovered that changes in DA receptor activity within the central nervous system are correlated with marked changes in glucose consumption in the lateral habenula, and thus probably in nerve cell activity of this area, emphasizing its important role in neural circuits regulated by DA receptors.

## Descending DA Neuron Systems

There are indications of minor DA projections from the A10 and A9 DA cell group to the locus ceruleus (NA cell group A6), to the lateral parabrachial nucleus, and to the cerebellum. Details of these descending DA projections are unknown. Evidence for the existence of DA cerebellar projection was also provided by the recent observation that probable $D_1$ receptors are found in the Purkinje cells of the cerebellum [40] (see Table 2).

### Diencephalospinal DA System

The diencephalospinal DA system originates mainly in the A11 DA cell group, which is located in the periventricular grey of the caudal thalamus and of the posterior and dorsal

hypothalamus (Fig. 5) [49]. These DA fibers descend along the lateral border of the central canal, in lamina I of Rexed and within the dorsolateral part of the lateral funiculus, and innervate the dorsal grey (laminae I–IV) of the cervical, thoracic, lumbar, and sacral spinal cord as well as the intermediolateral cell column of the spinal cord. The system would therefore seem to be involved in the regulation of activity in preganglionic sympathetic neurons. The DA innervation of the dorsal horn is found mainly in the lateral part of the superficial layers (laminae I–IV).

The A11 DA cell bodies also give rise to a few ascending branches innervating the medial and midline thalamus and several hypothalamic nuclei running within the periventricular catecholamine pathways.

### Vagal Preganglionic DA Neurons

In the caudal and medial part of the dorsal motor nucleus of the vagus there is a population of cholinergic preganglionic neurons which project to the thoracic viscera, probably mainly the heart, and which presumably also contain DA (Tables 2, 4). DA may therefore be a comodulator in the cholinergic synapses of the sinoatrial node.

## Local DA Neuron Systems of the Midbrain, Hypothalamus, and the Preoptic Area (Table 3)

### Mesoencephalic Periaqueductal DA Neuron System

The mesoencephalic periaqueductal DA neuron system is present along the entire length of the periaqueductal grey

**Fig. 5.** *Drawing of a sagittal section of a rat brain modified from the atlas of Paxinos and Watson (1982) showing the location of hypothalamic and preoptic DA nerve cell bodies [42]. This drawing corresponds to levels 0–0.4 mm lateral to the midline. The location of DA cell bodies is indicated by **filled triangles**. The differences in the sizes of the triangles represent differences in the sizes of the cell bodies found in the different hypothalamic nuclei*

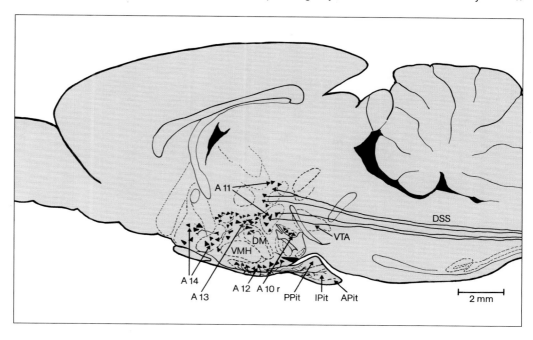

**Table 4.** *Local neurons of olfactory and optic systems*

| System | Origin | Innervation area |
|---|---|---|
| 1. Periglomerular DA neurons (A15) | Olfactor bulb | Dendritic processes into olfactory glomeruli |
| 2. Retinal DA system | Inner nuclear layer of the retina (amacrine cells) | Local dendritic processes |

and extends into the periventricular grey of the thalamus and the hypothalamus. The DA nerve cell bodies are small and probably give rise mainly to a local DA innervation of the periaqueductal grey. In addition, they may also contribute fibers to the periventricular DA system.

### Periventricular DA Neuron Systems of the Hypothalamus and the Preoptic Area

The periventricular DA cell bodies of the hypothalamus and the preoptic area are located along the entire dorso-ventral border of the periventricular grey (Fig. 5). The ventral component of this system belongs to group A 12, and the anterior hypothalamic periventricular system together with the preoptic periventricular system belongs to group A 14. These periventricular DA neurons are found at all rostrocaudal levels of the hypothalamus and the preoptic area. They give rise mainly to local DA innervation, e. g., of the anterior hypothalamus and the medial preoptic region.

### Incertohypothalamic DA Neuron System

The incertohypothalamic DA neuron system mainly originates in the medial zona incerta (group A 13) (Fig. 5). The cell group is densely packed and occupies the posterior part of the zona incerta. It gives rise mainly to a local DA innervation and to periventricular fibers that innervate the septum, periventricular hypothalamus, medial preoptic area, and anterior hypothalamus.

### Tuberoinfundibular and Tuberohypophyseal DA Neuron Systems

The tuberoinfundibular and tuberohypophyseal DA systems originate mainly in DA cell bodies of the arcuate and periarcuate nucleus and the ventral periventricular hypothalamic nucleus (Figs. 5, 6). Together they form what is called the A 12 DA system. The tuberoinfundibular DA neurons densely innervate the external layer of the median eminence and of the infundibular stalk. The tuberohypophyseal DA neuron system has its main origin in the anterior part of the group A 12 and innervates the entire pars intermedia and the posterior pituitary gland (mainly the part close to the infundibular stalk).

It appears likely that neuropeptides such as neurotensin and galanin may be comodulators in certain populations of tuberoinfundibular DA neurons, thus implicating neuropeptides as comodulators in various types of DA pathways. The DA nerve terminal networks of the median eminence and the infundibular stalk are very important regulators of the secretion of a number of hypothalamic hormones from the median eminence. They thus constitute an important component of the local circuits of the external layer, the integrative activity of which is responsible

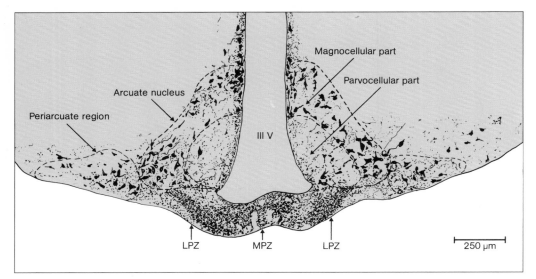

**Fig. 6.** *Drawing of the median eminence and the arcuate nucleus at the midhypothalamic level, showing the location of DA neuronal perikarya (**large profiles**) and nerve terminals (**small profiles**). This drawing was made from an overlay of a photomontage of photomicrographs of the section showing TH immunoreactivity. PAP technique, TH antiserum 1 : 1000. The adjacent section was stained with cresyl violet to determine the cytoarchitecture of this region. The arcuate nucleus could be easily divided into a magnocellular and parvocellular region in the Nissl-stained section. Notice that the DA neurons are located almost exclusively in the magnocellular and periarcuate region, whereas the parvocellular region contains predominantly DA nerve terminals. The subdivision of the adjacent region into the periarcuate region was based on cytoarchitectonic criteria and on the presence of distinctly different morphologic types of DA neurons. Notice the dense collection of DA nerve terminals in the median eminence, especially in the **LPZ***

for proper regulation of hypothalamic hormone release. In addition, DA itself is released from the medial palisade zone (MPZ) of the median eminence as a prolacting inhibitory factor which inhibits secretion of prolactin via activation of a D2 receptor located on the prolactin secreting cells of the anterior pituitary. Within the median eminence DA exerts an inhibitory action on the release of luteinizing hormone releasing hormone (LHRH) and thyrotropin releasing hormone (TRH) and on somatostatin secretion (see below). The DA nerve terminals in the pars intermedia have been suggested to reduce the secretion of $\alpha$-melanocyte stimulating hormone ($\alpha$MSH) from this region of the pituitary (see below). Furthermore, the tuberohypophyseal DA neurons seem to be selectively stimulated by dehydration, possibly via changes in the sodium concentration in the plasma [37], indicating a role in the regulation of vasopressin release (see below).

**Other Types of Hypothalamic DA Cell Groups**

In addition to the above-mentioned hypothalamic DA neuronal systems, DA cell groups are present in the dorsomedial hypothalamic nucleus, the area surrounding the paraventricular hypothalamic nucleus and the fornix, in the supramammillary area, along the ventral surface of the hypothalamus, and ventrally of the fornix in the border area between the medial and lateral hypothalamus. All these DA cell groups have been discovered principally by means of tyrosine hydroxylase immunocytochemistry. Their exact projections of are unknown, but they are prob-

ably mostly local neuronal systems. The presence of these large numbers of DA cell groups underlines the important role DA plays in the regulation of a number of hypothalamic nuclei and thus of large numbers of hypothalamic functions.

**Local DA Neurons of the Olfactory and Optic System (Table 4)**

The DA cell bodies in the olfactory bulb, (group A15) [25], are mostly periglomerular DA neurons which, via their dendritic processes, regulate activity in the olfactory glomeruli. The DA system within the retina is composed mainly of amacrine cells located principally in the inner nuclear layer and modulating retinal functions via local dendritic projections [33, 34].

**Studies on the Postsynaptic Regulation of DA Mechanisms: Evidence for Receptor-Receptor Interactions at the Local Circuit Level and at the Comodulator Level**

In vitro experiments have indicated that CCK-DA, neurotensin-DA, and glutamate-DA receptors can interact in various forebrain areas leading to a marked increase of

**Fig. 7.** *Schematic illustration of a DA synapse as an electrometabolic integrative unit, showing multiple transmission lines*

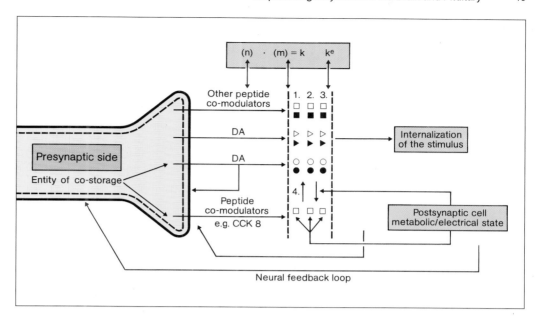

synaptic plasticity, in this case in the decoding of the DA receptors in DA synapses [1, 2, 3, 19, 20]. Consistent with these findings has been the demonstration that glutamate terminals and DA terminals project onto the same dentritic spines of striatal nerve cells, thus underlining the existence of receptor-receptor interactions at the local circuit level.

### On the Functional Role of DA Comodulators

CCK peptides coexist with DA in part of the subcortical limbic DA nerve terminal networks. It was therefore of considerable interest to demonstrate that the effect of CCK-8 on the binding characteristics of $^3$H-dopamine agonist binding sites is more marked in this region than in striatum. Thus, CCK-8 (10 n$M$) in subcortical limbic membranes can procude a more marked reduction of affinity than it does in striatal membranes, possibly because of an improved space- and time-locked interaction. Thus, one possible functional interpretation of the CCK peptides in DA nerve terminals may be as a regulator of the decoding system of the main transmission line, i.e., of the DA transmission line [2, 19]. This view is supported by the observations that CCK peptides given intraventricularly cannot modulate DA turnover in the CCK-DA costoring terminals of the subcortical limbic forebrain. In contrast, CCK peptides produce reductions of DA turnover in the diffuse types of DA terminals, which do not costore CCK peptides, which form the majority of the DA nerve-terminal populations in the forebrain. Thus, CCK peptides as modulators in local circuits can regulate DA release and turnover, but not in their function as DA comodulators. As comodulators, their function seems to be to change the decoding mechanism for the DA transmission line without inducing any changes in the homeostasis of the DA synapses, i.e., without inducing any changes in DA turnover

and release. In this way a *heterostatic* regulation of DA synapses becomes possible, allowing the changing of the set-point of the synapse without interfering with homeostatic mechanisms. Also, it must be emphasized that the existence of multiple transmission lines within each individual DA synapse (Fig. 7) makes possible a marked increase in the information transfer, i.e., in the number of messages reaching the postsynaptic elements. At the same time it becomes easier to understand the plastic changes occurring in DA networks, e.g., during their progressive degeneration in Parkinson's disease (see below).

### On the Functional Role of the Nigrostriatal and Mesolimbic DA Systems

#### DA Receptor Subclassification

There are two main classes of DA receptors: the $D_1$ type, which activates adenylate cyclase, and the $D_2$ type, which is negatively coupled to the adenylate cyclase or is unrelated to this enzyme (see fig. 8) [11, 12, 31, 46, 47]. The $D_1$ and $D_2$ types of DA receptor can exist in a high or a low affinity state for DA. Guanyl nucleotides favor the low affinity state. The $D_2$ receptor seems to be responsible for most of the behavioral effects of DA receptor agonists, such as stereotypical, locomotion and vomiting, as well as for their antipsychotic activity. It should be emphasized that DA receptor antagonists of the butyrophenone and benzamide type have a high to very high apparent affinity for the $D_2$ type of DA receptor, while they display only a very low to low apparent affinity for the $D_1$ receptor. There are also indications for subclasses of $D_1$ and $D_2$ receptors. The DA receptors in the anterior pituitary gland inhibiting the se-

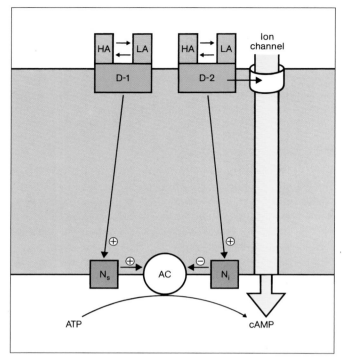

**Fig. 8.** *Summary of DA receptor classification and coupling to AC and ion channels. The D₁ subtype is also characterized by micromolar affinity for DA-receptor-blocking agents of the butyrophenone type (e. g., spiperone) and by lack of affinity for substituted benzamides such as (±) sulpiride. The D₂ subtype is characterized by nanomolar affinity for spiperone and by substantial affinity for the DA-receptor-blocking agent (±) sulpiride. Stimulatory (Ns) and inhibitory (Ni) guanyl-nucleotide binding proteins.*

cretion of prolactin are of the $D_2$ type. Also, the DA auto-receptors [7, 9] which are located on the DA neurons themselves and respond to DA are of the $D_2$ type. The DA autoreceptors are located in the nerve cell membrane of nerve terminals, cell bodies, and dendrites of both nigrostriatal and mesolimbic DA neurons. However, relatively few seem to exist in the nerve cell membranes of the cortical DA neurons projecting to the prefrontal cortex and the cingulate cortex [7]. The DA autoreceptors located in DA cell bodies and dendrites mainly control the firing rate in the DA neurons (impulse regulating somatodendritic autoreceptors), whereas terminal DA autoreceptors only exercise inhibitory modulation of DA synthesis and release (synthesis- and/or release-modulating terminal autoreceptors).

## Evidence for Involvement in Motor Control

The corpus striatum mainly exerts an inhibitory action on movement and thus makes possible the selection of meaningful behavior in a complex environment [14, 38]. The substantia nigra, in contrast, exerts an activating action on movement. This activation is mediated via the nigrostriatal DA system. Hence, degeneration of mesostriatal DA neurons or treatment with DA receptor blocking agents leads to the development of rigidity, hypokinesia, and tremor.

The activity of DA receptors in the striatum is therefore of fundamental importance in the maintenance of a normal posture and for the induction of normal movements. Consequently, treatment with DA receptor agonists or l-dopa stops tremor, induces movement, and reduces rigidity in Parkinsonian patients. Overactivation of DA receptors, which is easily induced in these patients, owing to the development of DA receptor supersensitivity in response to the denervation of the DA receptors, results in the development of involuntary movements, usually of a highly stereotyped character. Reduction in muscle tone and reduced ability to control posture have also been observed. The available experimental evidence indicates that when the DA networks in the nucleus caudatus and putamen (i. e., the *dorsal* striatum) are activated, rigidity and tremor are counteracted, while activation of DA receptors in the ventral striatum, especially the nucleus accumbens, counteracts the akinesia in Parkinson's disease and induces locomotion. Thus, it seems that the nigrostriatal and mesolimbic DA neurons have a differential role in the regulation of posture and movement. DA receptor activity in the ventral striatum mainly regulates movement, whereas tone and posture are regulated primarily via the dorsal striatal DA networks. One probable role of the DA neuron networks within the dorsal and ventral striatum is to decode various types of sensory stimuli, a process necessary for proper sensory motor integration, and hence for motor function. Thus, the degeneration of the ascending DA pathways to the striatum results in a sensory neglect contralateral to the side of the degeneration.

In view of this, it is generally considered that the Parkinsonian syndrome is produced by a state of striatal dominance due to the degeneration of the mesostriatal DA systems, which inhibits activity in the striatum. On treatment with l-dopa and DA receptor agonists, the substantia nigra of Parkinsonian patients may become dominant instead, and the inhibitory influence of the striatum on motility is abolished, leading to the development of involuntary movements. These abnormal involuntary movements are very similar to those found in Huntington's chorea, a disease in which striatal nerve cells degenerate.

In order to understand the development of Parkinson's disease it is important to recognize the high redundancy of DA mechanisms in the striatum. Thus, the Parkinsonian-like symptoms appear only when the extent of DA nerve terminal degeneration approaches 80%. It appears as though each discrete striatal DA nerve terminal population belonging to one DA nerve cell body in the midbrain is capable of subserving a large number of integrative functions within the striatum. Such complex tasks can probably be performed by each of the individual DA nerve terminal networks because of the existence of multiple transmission lines in the DA synapses, as indicated above. It must also be borne in mind that the remaining DA nerve cells increase their firing rate considerably, leading to increased DA release from remaining intact DA nerve terminals. Furthermore, this increased presynaptic DA release is matched by a development of DA receptor supersensitivity on the postsynaptic side. Thus, an increased density of DA receptors is observed, and these receptors probably have an increased coupling to the biological effectors, leading to an increased gain of the amplifier to the biological response.

In view of the current problems with chronic l-dopa therapy, which lead to the development of hyperkinesias and on-off effects, as well as to a reduction of the beneficial effects, new therapeutic approaches are required in Parkinson's disease. The present problems are probably partly related to the fact that l-dopa, via the formation of DA, is used as a hormone to correct the DA deficit which exists in a neuronal but not in a humoral control mechanism, and partly because chronic treatment with l-dopa may lead to abnormal changes in the decoding mechanisms of the supersensitive DA receptors. In light of our present knowledge of the complexity of the synaptic transmission, some therapeutic approaches in Parkinson's disease may be suggested. DA comodulators should be administered to control the gain of the decoding system of the supersensitive DA receptor complex in the striatal nerve cells. In addition, development of new DA agonists should be directed towards such agonists as selectively activate postsynaptic supersensitive DA receptors. Also, trophic factors should be administered which would stimulate collateral sprouting from the remaining DA terminals in striatum and also prolong the survival of the degenerating DA nerve cells.

## Mesolimbic and Mesolimbocortical DA Neurons and Their Possible Functional Role

The mesolimbic DA neurons innervating the ventral striatum not only have motor functions, as indicated above (induction of locomotor activity, anterior nucleus accumbens), but also may play a role in the regulation of emotional behavior. Anatomically, the ventral striatum is innervated by prefrontal and limbic cortical areas (see above), and therefore the DA nerve terminal networks in the ventral striatum play an important part in the integrative mechanisms involving limbic and prefrontal cortex microcircuits.

The mesolimbocortical DA neurons are also important in the regulation of activity in subcortical and cortical limbic regions. These neurons have been implicated in positive reinforcement. Lesions of these DA systems, especially of those to the prefrontal cortex, lead to locomotor hyperactivity. It has been speculated that this hyperactive syndrome may have some resemblance to the hyperactive syndrome found in children, which can be treated with amphetamine, a releaser of DA stores. Furthermore, electroshock can markedly increase DA turnover in the anteromedial frontal cortex (prefrontal cortex).

Antischizophrenic drugs have the common property of blocking central DA receptors. It has been suggested that

blockade, especially of limbic and prefrontal cortical DA receptors, but also of limbic subcortical receptors, might be the mode of action for the therapeutic effects of antipsychotic compounds. In agreement with this view is the observation that antipsychotic drugs produce different responses in the mesolimbocortical DA neurons, especially in the DA terminal networks in the prefrontal cortex. Thus, acute haloperidol treatment increases DA turnover only moderately within the mesocortical DA neurons and produces marked increases in the nigrostriatal and mesolimbic DA systems. Further, with chronic administration, tolerance to this action develops in the nigrostriatal and mesolimbic DA neurons and to a lesser extent in the mesolimbocortical DA systems, especially those in the frontal cortex. It has been suggested that the lack of tolerance to antipsychotic drugs in the mesocortical DA neurons may be related to an absence of DA autoreceptors on the DA terminals. In this way, no supersensitivity of a presynaptic DA receptor reducing DA release can be expected. Such a phenomenon would otherwise lead to further enhancement of the development of postsynaptic DA receptor supersensitivity owing to additional loss of DA receptor activity. A sustained DA receptor blockade may therefore exist within the limbic cortex and the prefrontal cortex, leading to a maintenance of antipsychotic action, while the rapid development of postsynaptic DA receptor supersensitivity in the nigrostriatal and mesolimbic DA systems lead to the development of resistance to the DA receptor blocking action of antipsychotic compounds. This phenomenon may greatly contribute to the onset of the tardive dyskinesias seen with chronic treatment with antischizophrenic drugs.

The new atypical antipsychotic compounds of the substituted benzamide type, such as l-sulpiride, have the ability to block the $D_2$ type of DA receptors selectively. It may be inferred that in the schizophrenic brain there may be abnormal decoding of the DA transmission line which operates via $D_2$ receptors, although central $D_1$ receptors may very well also be involved. Some investigators have found an increased number of $D_2$ receptors in the dorsal and ventral striatum in the schizophrenic brain.

## Tuberoinfundibular DA Neurons and Their Role in Regulating Secretion of Hormones from the Anterior Pituitary Gland

### Inhibitory DA Control of LHRH Secretion from the Median Eminence

The function of the tuberoinfundibular DA neurons in the LPZ (lateral palisade zone) and the MPZ has been evaluated, inter alia, by measuring DA turnover or DA synthesis in states with low and high secretion of LH [5, 16, 18, 21, 37]. As a rule, the DA turnover and synthesis in the LPZ is reduced in states with a high secretion of LH, indicating an

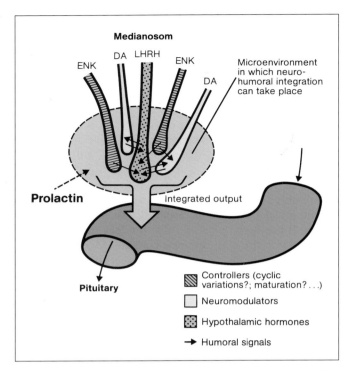

**Fig. 9.** *Schematic illustration of an LHRH medianosome in the median eminence*

inhibitory role of DA in the regulation of LHRH release. Furthermore, LHRH and DA nerve terminal networks in the LPZ largely overlap, and LHRH injected i. v. in the hypophysectomized male rat can selectively increase DA turnover in the LPZ. Thus, it seems that the ultrashort feedback action of LHRH on its own secretion may involve an activation of DA release from the adjacent DA nerve terminals, probably via reciprocal synapses. Gonadal steroids such as estrogens, and androgens under conditions in which they exert an inhibitory feedback action on LHRH release, also increase DA turnover in the LPZ [22]. This is supported by the demonstration that labeled estrogen accumulates in approximately half of the arcuate DA nerve cell bodies. In this way the transcription of certain types of messenger RNA may be markedly changed, leading to changes in the synthesis of receptor proteins, which in turn regulate the excitability of the DA cell body population. Also, pharmacologic studies in mammals and man provide evidence of an inhibitory regulation of LHRH release involving predominantly DA receptors of the $D_1$ type.

With a certain delay, prolactin hypersecretion also markedly increases DA turnover in the LPZ of the median eminence, an action which may be mediated via receptors for prolactin-like peptides present in the cell body areas of the arcuate DA neurons. This finding may explain why hyperprolactinemia in man and animals is associated with a reduction of LH secretion and blockade of ovulation, leading to amenorrhea and infertility. Taken together, the morphologic and functional studies indicate the existence of a rostrocaudal strip in the LPZ in which LHRH release is regulated by DA, prolactin, and probably enkephalin peptides, which also have the ability to inhibit LHRH secretion. Therefore, we have postulated the "medianosome," a domain of local circuits in the external layer of the median eminence, in which hormonal and electrical signals integrate to regulate a specific axis of the endocrine system (Fig. 9). This hypothesis claims that the external layer of the median eminence is built up of such medianosomes, making possible a proper decoding of the signals for hypothalamic hormone release [18, 21].

## Tuberoinfundibular DA Neurons and Prolactin Secretion

A large number of DA turnover studies indicate that DA is released from the MPZ of the median eminence as a prolactin inhibitory factor. It inhibits the secretion of prolactin via activation of $D_2$ receptors located on the prolactin secreting cells [6, 18, 21]. Thus, in the hypophysectomized rat, prolactin in the physiologic range can selectively and rapidly increase DA turnover in the MPZ. It therefore seems possible that the membrane of the MPZ DA terminals may contain receptors for prolactin-like peptides. Thus prolactin, which may reach the median eminence area via retrograde transport mechanisms in the infundibular stem, may induce its own rapid feedback action on the median eminence via direct regulation of DA release. It seems that prolactin is capable of inducing long-lasting increases in DA turnover in both MPZ and LPZ which outlast the increase in blood levels produced by a prolactin injection.

## Inhibitory DA Regulation of Somatostatin Secretion from the Median Eminence

In mammals and man, tuberoinfundibular DA nerve terminals in both the MPZ and LPZ seem to exert an inhibitory action on the release of somatostatin [5, 21]. Thus, DA receptor agonists increase growth hormone (GH) secretion. Furthermore, GH injections into the hypophysectomized male rat reduce DA turnover in the MPZ and LPZ. Injections of somatostatin into the hypophysectomized male rat induce an opposite response, i.e., they increase DA turnover in the MPZ and LPZ. Thus there may be somatostatin-DA interaction in the MPZ and LPZ of the median eminence, and DA seems to mediate the ultrashort feedback action of somatostatin on its own release and also the short feedback action of GH. Thus, DA terminals play an important role in the inhibitory regulation of somatostatin secretion from the median eminence. They establish reciprocal synapses with the somatostatin bouton and may have GH receptors on their membranes. DA nerve terminals are therefore important in the local circuits regulating somatostatin secretion in the median eminence (somatostatin "medianosome"), since they make possible an integration of humoral and electrical signals in the regulation of GH secretion. Paradoxically, DA receptor agonists, such as bromocriptine, reduce GH secretion in acromegaly, probably because of the existence of receptors for DA on the hyperplastic gland cells containing GH. It must be emphasized that intact GH-containing gland cells of healthy men also possess DA receptors that inhibit the secretion of GH [35]. However, in spite of this fact, DA agonists increase GH secretion in healthy men, probably through an action on hypothalamic DA receptors controlling somatostatin and/or GHRH release, leading to reduced somatostatin release and increased GHRH release [30] from the median eminence. In this way the inhibitory action of DA on DA receptors in the anterior pituitary gland can be masked and replaced by a stimulation of GH release. The difference explains the important therapeutic action of bromocriptine in acromegaly.

## Inhibitory DA Regulation of TRH Secretion from the Median Eminence

Pharmacologic studies indicate that DA can inhibit the secretion of TRH. Furthermore, thyroidectomy reduces DA turnover selectively in the external layer of the median eminence in both the MPZ and LPZ [5]. TRH given i.v. in the hypophysectomized male rat increases DA turnover in the MPZ and LPZ of the median eminence. Rat TSH also induces an increase in DA turnover in the MPZ and LPZ, as does chronic treatment with thyroid hormones. Together, these results indicate that DA nerve terminals in the median eminence also play an important role in the local circuits regulating the secretion of TRH (the TRH medianosome). Again, the DA nerve terminal networks seem to make possible an integration of hormonal and electrical signals in the TRH medianosome so that a proper decoding of the signals controlling TRH release can occur.

There is thus evidence that the tuberoinfundibular DA neurons participate in an important inhibitory way in regulating the release of LHRH, somatostatin, and TRH from the median eminence, and that the DA nerve terminals of the MPZ release DA as a prolactin inhibiting factor.

## Tuberohypophyseal DA Neuron Systems and Their Role in Regulating Secretion of Hormones from the Pars Intermedia of the Anterior Pituitary Gland

The intermediate lobe of the pituitary gland is a homogeneous population of cells which contain and secrete peptides related to ACTH, especially $\alpha$MSH, and to lipotropin. All these peptides derive from proopiocortin, a common glycoprotein precursor. A number of studies have shown that there is a $D_2$ DA receptor in the intermediate lobe of rat pituitary gland [10, 45]. The results indicate that, when activated, the $D_2$ DA receptor produces an inhibition of basal cAMP accumulation, indicating that the $D_2$ type of DA receptor in the intermediate lobe is negatively coupled to adenylate cyclase [10, 36]. Further, the ability of DA agonists to reduce the accumulation of cAMP is related to

their ability to reduce the secretion of $\alpha$MSH from the intermediate lobe. Finally, it has been shown that the $D_2$ DA receptor mediated inhibition of adenylate cyclase activity in the intermediate lobe requires guanosine 5-triphosphate (GTP) [10]. Thus, the tuberohypophyseal DA neurons exert an inhibitory action on the release of $\alpha$MSH in the intermediate lobe, an action controlled by a $D_2$ DA receptor operating through an inhibitory regulation of cAMP accumulation via a guanyl nucleotide-dependent regulatory coupling protein. $\alpha$MSH exerts an inhibitory feedback action on its own secretion by increasing activity in the arcuate DA cells. This inhibitory DA control is opposed by a humoral catecholamine adrenergic mechanism which operates via $\beta_2$-adrenergic receptors located on the gland cells of the pars intermedia and which stimulates cAMP accumulation and $\alpha$MSH secretion. This $\beta_2$-adrenergic receptor is probably activated by catecholamines in the blood that originate from the adrenal medulla.

The mechanism of $\beta$-endorphin release from the intermediate lobe of the rat pituitary gland has also been evaluated. Here too, it has been shown that DA inhibits the release of $\beta$-endorphin, while the $\alpha$-adrenoreceptor in the intermediate lobe enhances the release of $\beta$-endorphin-like activity [16, 48]. Further, DA antagonists elevate the plasma $\beta$-endorphin immunoreactivity, indicating that the pituitary $\beta$-endorphin secretion is tonically inhibited by DA released from the tuberohypophyseal DA neurons. These neurons therefore act as inhibitory controllers of the secretion of $\alpha$MSH and $\beta$-endorphin, two important stress hormones.

## Hypothalamic DA Neuron Systems and Their Role in Regulating Secretion of Hormones from the Posterior Pituitary Gland

Two types of DA neuron system are probably involved in the regulation of the secretion of vasopressin and oxytocin from the posterior pituitary gland. Thus, there is evidence for the presence of DA interneurons within and around the paraventricular hypothalamic nucleus and supraoptic nucleus which may control activity in the oxytocin and vasopressin neuron systems by an action at the cell body dendritic level. There are also tuberohypophyseal DA neurons which directly innervate the posterior pituitary gland. The central effects of DA on vasopressin release have been evaluated in the normally hydrated and the water-loaded rat. It was found that DA given i.v.t. enhances the secretion of vasopressin, leading to the production of a dose-dependent antidiuresis [15]. It has further been shown that DA exerts excitatory effects on the reflex release of vasopressin in the rat [39]. Studies on electrical unit activity of vasopressinergic cells in the paraventricular nucleus suggested that there is an excitatory DA mechanism operating at the level of this nucleus, controlling activity in vasopressinergic cells. However, in studies on the actions of DA on the electrically stimulated neurohypophyseal release of vasopressin in vitro, evidence has been obtained of a direct inhibitory action of DA on the vasopressinergic nerve terminals [32]. Thus, the DA nerve terminal systems innervating the posterior pituitary gland (tuberohypophyseal DA neurons) may constitute an inhibitory DA mechanism operating at the level of the vasopressinergic nerve terminals.

Oxytocinergic nerve cells also appear to be controlled by an excitatory DA mechanism operating at the level of the paraventricular hypothalamic nucleus [39]. Thus, in studies on the effects of i.v.t. injections of DA agonists and antagonists it could be shown that DA and apomorphine facilitated and established the milk ejection reflex. Furthermore, DA receptor antagonists prevented the reflex activation of oxytocin immunoreactive nerve cell induced by suckling. Thus, the DA mechanism operating in the paraventricular hypothalamic nucleus may control, in an excitatory way, the periodic activation of oxytocinergic cells during suckling.

**Acknowledgements.** We are very grateful to Mrs A. Edgren for excellent secretarial assistance and to Miss M. B. Maggs of Basel for assistance in preparing the manuscript.

# References

1. Agnati LF, Celani MF, Fuxe K (1983) Cholecystokinin peptides in vitro modulate the characteristics of the striatal ³H-N-propyl-norapomorphine sites. Acta Physiol Scand 118: 79–81

2. Agnati LF, Fuxe K, Benfenati F, Battistini N, Zini I, Camurri M, Hökfelt T (1984) Postsynaptic effects of neuropeptide comodulators at central monoamine synapses. In: 5th International catecholamine symposium, june 12–16, Göteborg, Sweden. Scientific, medical and scholarly publications. Liss, New York

3. Agnati LF, Fuxe K, Benfenati F, Celani MF, Battistini F, Mutt V, Cavicchioli L, Galli G, Hökfelt T (1983) Differential modulation by CCK-8 and CCK-4 of ³H-spiperone binding sites linked to DA and 5-hydroxytryptamine receptors in the brain of the rat. Neurosci Lett 35: 179–198

4. Andén N-E, Dahlström A, Fuxe K, Larsson K, Olson L, Ungerstedt U (1966) Ascending monoamine neurons to the telencephalon and diencephalon. Acta Physiol Scand 67: 313–326

5. Andersson K, Fuxe K, Eneroth P, Agnati LF, Locatelli V (1980) Hypothalamic DA and noradrenaline nerve terminal systems and their reactivity of changes in pituitary-thyroid and pituitary-adrenal activity and to prolactin. In: Brambilla F, Racagni G, de Wied D (eds) Progress in psychoneuroendocrinology. Elsevier, Amsterdam, pp 395–406

6. Andersson K, Fuxe K, Eneroth P, Nyberg P, Roos P (1981) Rat prolactin and hypothalamic catecholamine nerve terminal systems: evidence for rapid and discrete increases in DA and noradrenalin turnover in the hypophysectomized male rat. Eur J Pharmacol 76: 261–265

7. Bannon MJ, Chiodo LA, Bunney EB, Wolf ME, Grace AA, Bunney BS, Roth RH (1984) In vivo biochemical and electrophysiological studies on the distribution and pharmacology of DA autoreceptors. In: Usdin E, Carlsson A, Dahlström A, Engel J (eds) Neurology and neurobiology. Catecholamines part B: neuro-

pharmacology and central nervous system-theoretical aspects. Liss, New York, pp 25–42

8. Carlsson A, Falck B, Hillarp N-Å (1962) Cellular localization of brain monoamines. Acta Physiol Scand [Suppl] 196: 1–27

9. Carlsson A (1975) Receptor mediated control of DA metabolism. In Usdin E, Bunney WE (eds) Catecholamines: basic and clinical frontiers, Dekker, New York, pp 49–65

10. Cote TE, Grewe CW, Tsuruta K, Stoof JC, Eskay RL, Kebabian JW (1982) D-2 DA receptor-mediated inhibition of adenylate cyclase activity in the intermediate lobe of the rat pituitary gland requires guanosine 5′-triphosphate. Endocrinology 110: 812–819

11. Creese I, Usdin TB, Snyder SH (1979) Dopamine receptor binding regulated by guanine nucleotides. Mol Pharmacol 16: 69–76

12. Creese I, Sibley DR, Hamblin MW, Leff SE (1983) The classification of DA receptors: relationship to radioligand binding. Annu Rev Neurosci 6: 43–71

13. Dahlström A, Fuxe K (1964) Evidence for the existence of monoamine-containing neurons in the central nervous system. I. Demonstration of monoamines in the cell bodies of brain stem neurons. Acta Physiol Scand [Suppl] 232: 1–55

14. Dray A (1980) The physiology and pharmacology of mammalian basal ganglia. Prog Neurobiol 14: 221

15. Forsling ML, Williams H (1984) Central effects of DA on vasopressin release in the normally hydrated and water-loaded rat. J Physiol (Lond) 346: 49–59

16. Furuki Y (1983) Mechanism of beta-endorphin release regulation-evaluation using dispersed cells of the pituitary intermediate lobe. Nippon Sanka Fujinka Gakkai Zasshi 9: 1604–1610

17. Fuxe K (1965) Evidence for the existence of monoamine neurons in the central nervous system. IV. Distribution of monoamine nerve terminals in the central nervous system. Acta Physiol Scand [Suppl] 247: 39–85

18. Fuxe K, Agnati LF, Andersson K, Locatelli V, Eneroth P, Hökfelt T, Mutt V, McDonald T, El Etreby MF, Zini I, Calza L (1980) Concepts in neuroendocrinology with emphasis on neuropeptide-monoamine interactions in neuroendocrine regulation. In: Brambilla F, Racagni G, de Wied D (eds) Progress in psychoneuroendocrinology. Elsevier, Amsterdam, pp 47–61

19. Fuxe K, Agnati LF, Benfenati F, Celani MF, Zini I, Zoli M, Mutt V (1983) Evidence for the existence of receptor-receptor interactions in the central nervous system. Studies on the regulation of monoamine receptors by neuropeptides. J Neural Transm 18: 165–179

20. Fuxe K, Agnati LF, Benfenati F, Cimmino M, Algeri S, Hökfelt T, Mutt V (1981) Modulation by cholecystokinins of ³H-spiroperidol binding in rat striatum: Evidence for increased affinity and reduction in the number of binding sites. Acta Physiol Scand 113: 541–548

21. Fuxe K, Agnati LF, Calza L, Andersson K, Giardino L, Benfenati F, Camurri M, Goldstein (1984) Quantitative chemical neuroanatomy gives new insights into the catecholamine regulation of the peptidergic neurons projecting to the median eminence. In: 5th International Catecholamine Symposium, June 12–16, Göteborg, Sweden. Scientific, medical and scholarly publications. Liss, New York

22. Fuxe K, Andersson K, Blake CA, Eneroth P, Gustafsson J-Å, Agnati LF (1981) Effects of estrogen and combined treatment with estrogen and progesterone on central DA, noradrenaline and adrenaline nerve terminal systems of the ovariectomized rat. Relationship of changes in amine turnover to changes in LH and prolactin secretion and in sexual behaviour. In: Fuxe K, Gustafsson J-Å, Wetterberg L (eds) Steroid hormone regulation of the brain. Pergamon, New York, pp 73–92

23. Fuxe K, Hökfelt T, Agnati LF, Johansson O, Goldstein M, Perez de la Mora, Possani L, Tapia R, Teran L, Palacios R (1978) Mapping out central catecholamine neurons: immunohistochemical studies on catecholamine-synthesizing enzymes. In: Lipton MA, DiMascio A, Killam KF (eds) Psychopharmacology: a generation of progess. Raven Press, New York

24. Fuxe K, Hökfelt T, Ungerstedt U (1970) Morphological and func-

tional aspects of central monoamine neurons. In: International review of neurobiology, vol 13. Academic Press, New York, p 93

25 Halász ZN, Ljungdahl Å, Hökfelt T, Johansson O, Goldstein M, Park D, Biberfeld P (1977) Transmitter-histochemistry of the rat olfactory bulb. I. Immunohistochemical localization of monoamine synthesizing enzymes: support for intrabulbar, periglomerular DA neurons. Brain Res 126: 455–474

26. Heimer L, Switzer RD, Van Hoesen GW (1982) Ventral striatum and ventral pallidum. Components of the motor system? TINS, March, p 83

27. Hökfelt T, Johansson O, Fuxe K, Goldstein M, Park D (1976) Immunohistochemical studies on the localization and distribution of monoamine neuron systems in the rat brain. I. Tyrosine hydroxylase in the mes- and diencephalon. Med Biol 54: 427–453

28. Hökfelt T, Ljungdahl Å, Fuxe K, Johansson O (1974) Dopamine nerve terminals in the rat limbic cortex: aspects of the DA hypothesis of schizophrenia. Science 184: 177–179

29. Hökfelt T, Skirboll L, Rehfeld JF, Goldstein M, Markey K, Dann O (1980) A subpopulation of mesencephalic DA neurons projecting to limbic areas contains a cholecystokinin-like peptide: Evidence from immunohistochemistry combined with retrograde tracting. Neuroscience 5: 2093–2124

30. Kakucska I, Makara GB (1983) Various putative neurotransmitters affect growth hormone (GH) release in rats with anterolateral hypothalamic differentiation of the medial basal hypothalamus: evidence for mediation by a GH-releasing factor. Endocrinology 113: 318–323

31. Kebabian JW, Calne DB (1979) Multiple receptors for DA. Nature 277: 93–96

32. Lightman SL, Iversen LL, Forsling ML (1982) Dopamin and [D-ALA 2, D-Leu 5] enkephalin inhibit the electrically stimulated neurohypophyseal release of vasopressin in vitro: evidence for calcium-dependent opiate action. J Neurosci 1: 78–81

33. Lindvall O, Björklund A (1978) Organization of catecholamine neurons in the rat central nervous system. In: Iversen LL, Iversen SD, Snyder SH (eds) Handbook of psychopharmacology, vol 9. Plenum Press, New York, p 139

34. Lindvall O, Björklund A (1983) Dopamine- and norepinephrine-containing neuron systems: their anatomy in the rat brain. In: Emson PC (ed) Chemical Neuroanatomy. Raven Press, New York, p 229

35. Marcovitz S, Goodyer CG, Guyda H, Gardiner RJ, Hardy J (1982) Comparative study of human fetal, normal adult, and somatotropic adenoma pituitary function in tissue culture. J Clin Endocrinol 54: 6–16

36. Meunier H, Labrie F (1982) The DA receptor in the intermediate lobe of the rat pituitary gland is negatively coupled to adenylate cyclase. Life Sci 11: 963–968

37. Moore K, Demarest K (1982) Tuberoinfundibular and tuberohypophyseal dopaminergic neurons. In: Ganong WF, Martini L (eds) Frontiers in neuroendocrinology, vol 7. Springer, Berlin Heidelberg New York, pp 161–190

38. Moore RY, Bloom FE (1978) Central catecholamine neuron systems: anatomy and physiology of the DA systems. Annu Rev Neurosci 1: 129–169

39. Moos F, Richard P (1982) Excitatory effect of DA on oxytocin and vasopressin reflex releases in the rat. Brain Res 2: 249–260

40. Ouimet C, Miller P, Hemmings H, Walaas S, Greengard P (1984) Darpp-32, a DA- and adenosine 3′:5′-monophosphate-regulated phosphoprotein enriched in dopamine-innervated brain regions. J Neurosci 4 (1) 111–124

41. Park D, Goldstein M (1976) Purification of tyrosine hydroxylase from pheochromocytoma tumors. Life Sci 18: 55–60

42. Paxinos G, Watson C (1982) The rat brain in stereotaxic coordinates. Academic Press, New York

43. Pearson J, Goldstein M, Markey K, Brandeis L (1983) Human brainstem catecholamine neuronal anatomy as indicated by immunocytochemistry with antibodies to tyrosine hydroxylase. Neuroscience 8: 3–32

44. Phillipson OT, Griffith AC (1980) The neurons of origin for the mesohabenular DA pathway. Brain Res 197: 213–218

45. Proulx-Ferland L, Meunier H, Cote J, Dumont D, Gagne B, Labrie F (1983) Multiple factors involved in the control of ACTH and alpha-MSH secretion. J Steroid Biochem 18: 439–445

46. Schwartz JC, Delandre M, Martres MP, Sokoloff P, Protais P, Vasse, Costentin J. Laibe P, Mann A, Wermuth CG, Gulat C, Laffite A (1984) Biochemical and behavioural identification of discriminant benzamide derivatives: New tools to differentiate subclasses of DA receptors. In: Usdin E, Carlsson A, Dahlström A, Engel J (eds) Neurology and neurobiology. Catecholamines part B: neuropharmacology and central nervous system – theoretical aspects. Liss, New York, pp 59–72

47. Seeman P (1981) Brain DA receptors. Pharmacol Rev 32: 29–313

48. Sharp B, Ross R, Levin E, Sowers J (1982) Dopamine regulates canine plasma beta-endorphin-immunoreactivity levels. Endocrinology 5: 1828–1830

49. Skagerberg G, Björklund A, Lindvall O, Schmidt RH (1982) Origin and termination of the diencephalo-spinal DA system in the rat. Brain Res Bull 9: 237–244

50. Ungerstedt U (1971) Stereotaxic mapping of the monoamine pathways in the rat brain. Acta Physiol Scand [Suppl] 367: 1–48

# The Role of Dopamine in the Periphery

**Barbara J. Clark**

*Cardiovascular Unit, Preclinical Research, Sandoz Ltd., Basle, Switzerland*

## Introduction

Almost all recent textbooks of physiology still adhere to the concept that acetylcholine and noradrenaline are the only postganglionic autonomic transmitters, although there is strong evidence that others may also exist. Candidates in which particular interest is being shown at present are the purine nucleotides, a variety of peptides, and the catecholamine dopamine.

Until comparatively recently, interest in dopamine was based largely on its position in the biosynthetic pathway of noradrenaline and adrenaline (Fig. 1). The essential amino acids phenylalanine and tyrosine, derived from proteins in the diet, form the starting point for catecholamine synthesis. These amino acids are slowly converted into dopa by the action of oxidizing enzymes present in the cell bodies of adrenergic neurones, in melanophore cells, and the adrenal medulla. The next step, the conversion of dopa to dopamine is a very efficient and fast reaction catalyzed by dopa decarboxylase. (This enzyme was first discovered in the kidney but also occurs in large amounts in the liver as well as in adrenergic neurones and chromaffin cells.) Dopamine is the first in the sequence of catecholamines. The synthetic pathway proceeds to the formation of noradrenaline in sympathetic nerves and certain neurones in the central nervous system, and finally to adrenaline in chromaffin cells.

Since dopamine is the immediate precursor of the adrenergic transmitter noradrenaline, the occurrence of small amounts of dopamine in sympathetically innervated organs is to be expected. Only very small quantities are found in the adrenal medulla and other chromaffin tissue,

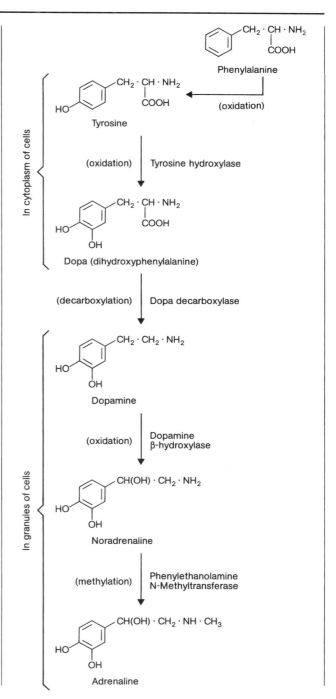

**Fig. 1.** *The main pathway in the synthesis of catecholamines. Enzyme systems that catalyze the formation of catecholamines are present in sympathetic adrenergic neurones, in neurones in parts of the central nervous system, in the adrenal medullae, and chromaffin cells in other tissues. In adrenergic neurones the enzymes are synthesized in the perinuclear region of the cell body. The terminal axons are the important sites of transmitter synthesis, and the enzymes are conveyed there by axonal transport of cytoplasm and organelles. The rate of synthesis of tyrosine hydroxylase is dependent on the amount of neuronal traffic and thereby controls the rate of synthesis of catecholamines*

Basic and Clinical Aspects of Neuroscience
Springer-Sandoz Advanced Texts
© by Springer-Verlag Berlin · Heidelberg 1985

where it is clearly present as a metabolic intermediate and is not stored. By contrast, the levels of dopamine detected in certain adrenergic nerves and sympathetic ganglia amount to as much as 30%–50% of the total catecholamine content. In some tissues, e.g. lung, bronchi, liver, intestine, pancreas and carotid body, the levels of dopamine even exceed those of noradrenaline (Table 1). Such observations are incompatible with the concept of dopamine being merely an intermediate in the biosynthesis of other catecholamines, and led Blaschko to suggest in 1957 that dopamine might have an independent physiological role in the periphery [9]. It had been shown 15 years previously that dopamine had an effect on blood pressure in the rabbit and guinea pig which was qualitatively different from that of adrenaline [30], but its generally low potency tended, until fairly recently, to discourage consideration of any independent biological function.

## Cardiovascular Effects of Dopamine

Dopamine was first synthesized in 1910. However, the few pharmacological investigations undertaken during the subsequent 50 years failed to detect any differences between its cardiovascular actions and those of noradrenaline and adrenaline that were interesting enough to warrant further study. The turning point came in the early 1960s when it was observed that the predominant effect of dopamine in man was to increase cardiac output and stroke volume, and reduce peripheral resistance. In this respect it resembled adrenaline, but unlike adrenaline, it did not increase heart rate. The effects also differed from those of noradrenaline, which produces marked increases in peripheral resistance and reflex bradycardia [35] (Table 2). Subsequent pharmacological studies in dogs showed that the actions of dopamine are, indeed, very different from those of the other catecholamines, and far more complex than had been supposed.

The amine is a potent cardiac stimulant. It increases myocardial contractility by a direct action on $\beta$-adrenoceptors, and also by releasing noradrenaline from cardiac sympathetic nerve terminals. The effects of dopamine on the heart contrast with those of a pure $\beta$-adrenoceptor stimulant, e.g. isoprenaline, in that marked increases in contractile force can be obtained at low doses in the absence of a simultaneous increase in heart rate (Fig. 2); heart rate, A-V conduction and excitability of the heart increase only at very high doses. Isoprenaline, on the other hand, induces parallel increases in the force and rate of contraction irrespective of the dose used.

Dopamine also has vasoconstrictor activity. At first this was thought to be due to stimulation of $\alpha$-adrenoceptors since responses could be blocked by phenoxybenzamine. But phenoxybenzamine is not a selective blocking agent, and later experiments in isolated tissues suggested that serotonin (5-HT) receptor stimulation might also be involved. Experiments in anaesthetized dogs revealed further differences between the actions of dopamine and those of other catecholamines. In barbiturate-anaesthetized animals, in which sympathetic tone is relatively low, dopamine increases systolic blood pressure dose-dependently, but at low doses, diastolic pressure is reduced (Fig. 2). When the vasoconstrictor effect of dopamine is eliminated with phenoxybenzamine, a depressor effect is unmasked, due principally to dilation of mesenteric and renal vessels. The dilator effect in these regions is not influenced by $\beta$-adrenoceptor and ganglion blocking agents, atropine, antihistamines and pretreatment with reserpine,

**Table 1.** *Tissue levels of dopamine (DA) and noradrenaline (NA) in animals and man (data taken from [6, 7, 33]). Note the high levels of dopamine in some tissues compared with the corresponding levels of noradrenaline. The ratio between the levels of a precursor and the substance formed from it should be the same in all tissues. Also the rank order of uptake of the two substances in different organs should be the same. When radioactive dopamine is injected intravenously into the guinea pig, however, the highest amounts accumulate in the kidneys, followed in decreasing order, by the lungs, liver, spleen, heart and plasma. By contrast, labelled noradrenaline accumulates (in decreasing order) in the spleen, lungs, heart, adrenals, kidneys, liver, small intestine and plasma. The difference in distribution of the two amines may be interpreted as evidence that they have independent physiological roles*

| Tissue | DA (µg/g tissue) | NA (µg/g tissue) | Species |
|---|---|---|---|
| Adrenal medulla | 0 | 314 | man |
|  | 17 | 1250 | cattle |
| Carotid body | 20–40 | 1.5 | rabbit |
| Ganglia: |  |  |  |
|   superior cervical | 0.82 | 5.25 | cat |
|   stellate | 1.32 | 2.82 | cat |
|   coeliac | 2.2 | 40.0 | dog |
|   renal | 2.0 | 26.4 | dog |
| Kidney: |  |  |  |
|   total | 0.07 | 0.3 | cat |
|   total | 0.03 | 0.3 | dog |
|   cortex | 0.08 | 0.34 | dog |
|   medulla | 0.03 | 0.21 | dog |
| Jejunum: |  |  |  |
|   total | 0.16 | 0.003 | dog |
|   mucosa | 0.20 | 0.003 | dog |
|   muscularis | 0.05 | – | dog |
| Colon | 0.30 | 0.02 | dog |
| Lung | 0.06 | 0.35 | dog |
|  | 0.60 | 0.14 | man |
| Mesenteric artery | 0.03 | 0.63 | dog |
| Heart: |  |  |  |
|   total | 0.16 | 0.67 | dog |
|   sinoatrial node | 2.06 | 1.89 | dog |
|   right atrium | 0.11 | 1.95 | dog |
|   left ventricle | 0.1 | 0.56 | dog |
| Plasma (ng/ml) | 0.98 | 1.55[a] | man |
|  | 1.60 | 0.76[a] | dog |
| Urine (ng/ml) | 473 | 168 | man |
|   (ng/ml) | 104 | 42 | dog |
|   (µg/24 h) | 100–700 | 10–100 | man |

[a] Noradrenaline and adrenaline

**Table 2.** *Haemodynamic effects of catecholamines in healthy subjects (i. v. infusions) and anaesthetized dogs (bolus i. v. injections). Increases in heart rate and myocardial contractile force produced by all four catecholamines, and the vasodilator effects of isoprenaline and adrenaline are due to β-adrenoceptor stimulation. Vasoconstriction is mediated via α-adrenoceptors. Dopamine decreases systemic resistance and dilates renal and mesenteric blood vessels by acting on receptors which are specific for the amine [23]*

| Effects in man | Dopamine | Adrenaline | Noradrenaline | Isoprenaline |
|---|---|---|---|---|
| Cardiac output | ↑↑ | ↑↑↑ | ↓ | ↑↑↑ |
| Heart rate | ↔ [a] | ↑↑ | ↓ | ↑↑↑ |
| Systemic resistance | ↓ | ↓↓ | ↑ | ↓↓↓ |
| Renal blood flow | ↑↑ | ↓↓ | ↓↓ | ↔↓ |
| *Cardiac actions in the dog* | | | | |
| Heart rate | increase[a] + | increase + + + | increase + + | increase + + + |
| Contractility | increase + + + | increase + + + | increase + + + | increase + + + |
| *Predominant action on vessels in the dog* | | | | |
| Skeletal muscle | constriction + | dilation or constriction[b] | constriction + + + | dilation + + + |
| Kidney | dilation + + + | constriction + + + | constriction + + + | dilation + |
| Intestine | dilation + + | dilation + + + | constriction + + + | dilation + + + |

The symbols  + ↑↓ indicate relative changes

[a] Dopamine increases heart rate at high doses; low doses produce no change or may decrease rate if sympathetic tone is high. Decreases are due to stimulation of neuronal dopamine receptors (vide infra)

[b] Adrenaline dilates vessels in skeletal muscle at low doses, but constricts at high doses

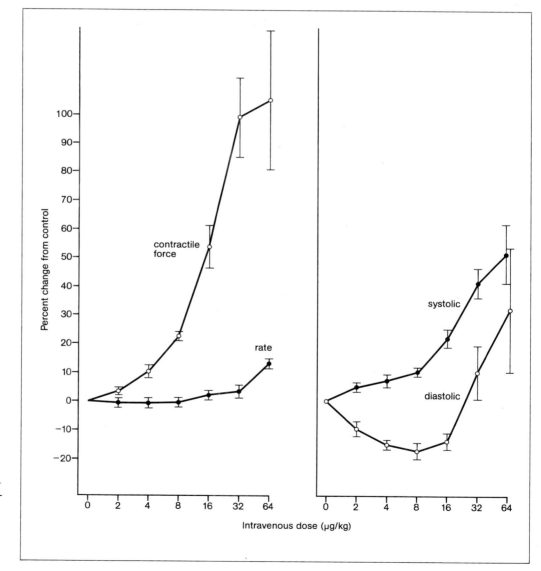

**Fig. 2.** *Mean effects (± SE) of increasing intravenous doses of dopamine on contractile force and heart rate, and systolic and diastolic pressure in 16 dogs anaesthetized with a mixture of pentobarbital and barbital [45]*

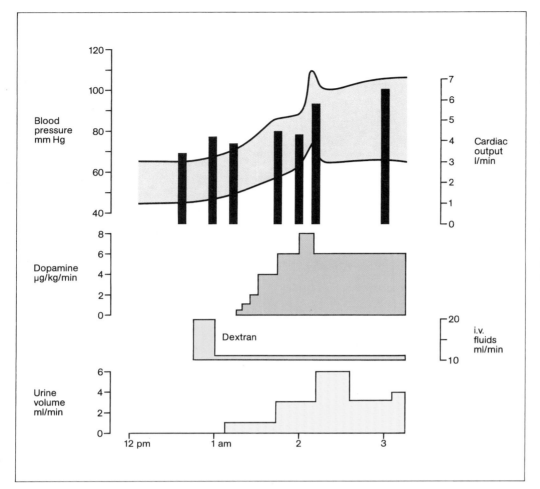

**Fig. 3.** *Effects of dopamine in a patient with pneumococcal meningitis, bacteraemia and hypotension. During the period shown, blood pressure was monitored from a punctured femoral artery, and cardiac output estimated by dye dilution. Previous administration of metaraminol had increased blood pressure, but the patient remained anuric. Intravenous infusion of 250 ml dextran over 10 min increased arterial and central venous pressures, raised cardiac output slightly, but failed to stimulate urine output. Subsequent administration of dopamine produced the cardiovascular and renal responses shown. The amine was infused for a further 18 h with no deterioration in cardiovascular status [43]*

but is selectively attenuated by neuroleptic compounds, which are known to block dopamine receptors in the central nervous system. The extensive work of Goldberg and his colleagues has led to the concept that the dilator effect of dopamine on renal and splanchnic vessels is due to stimulation of receptors which are specific for the amine [23].

Dopamine not only increases total renal blood flow, but changes the cortical:medullary perfusion ratio, increases glomerular filtration rate and enhances sodium excretion [23]. The unique profile of activity of dopamine on the cardiovascular system and renal function motivated Goldberg to initiate clinical trials in the treatment of shock (Fig. 3), congestive cardiac failure (Fig. 4), hypertension, oligouric renal failure and drug intoxication [23, 49].

## Vascular Receptors

Goldberg's pioneering work stimulated many investigations into the location and function of dopamine receptors in the periphery. Some were unfortunately performed un-

der less than ideal conditions with the result that a number of the effects of dopamine have been attributed to dopamine receptor stimulation when they could equally well have been due to actions on α- or β-adrenoceptors.

Historically, classification of a receptor by physiological techniques has depended on demonstrating a rank order of potency for a series of agonists and antagonists, which must be the same in all tissues or organs considered to have the same receptor. Specific antagonism must also be demonstrated, i.e. the antagonist should inhibit or prevent the effect of a drug stimulating the receptor in question at a dose (or concentration) which does not affect responses to drugs acting via different mechanisms. Ideally, such investigations should be done under steady state conditions in order to obtain precise quantitation of responses. These criteria can only be fulfilled in isolated tissue preparations. All of the early investigations on the cardiovascular actions of dopamine were conducted in intact animals or in man. These studies were invaluable in providing the basis for assuming the presence of specific receptors but did not give proof of their existence. The vasodilating action of dopamine could have been due, for example, to the release of another vasodilating substance such as a kinin or a prostaglandin or to production of an unknown metabo-

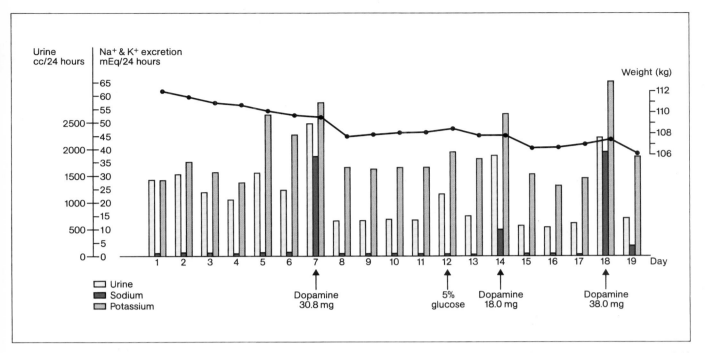

**Fig. 4.** *Effects of intravenous infusions of dopamine or 5% glucose in water in a patient with hypertensive cardiovascular disease and congestive cardiac failure. The patient was placed on a diet containing 200 mg sodium and allowed a maximum of 1000 ml distilled water daily. All drugs except digoxin and warfarin were withdrawn for the duration of the 19-day study. The three doses of dopamine were infused over periods of 170, 180 and 240 min respectively [26]*

lite of dopamine. Research was severely hampered by the lack of suitable in vitro models, and the lack of really selective dopamine receptor stimulants and blocking agents. It is only during recent years that these difficulties have been overcome.

Experiments in isolated tissues have now established beyond doubt that dopamine receptors are present in vascular smooth muscle [12, 50]. They have also confirmed observations made in intact animals that their distribution is far from homogeneous. Although there is evidence for their presence in limited numbers in the limb vasculature of the dog, dopamine receptors are largely confined to four major vascular beds – the renal, splanchnic, coronary and cerebral [12, 23, 50]. Their very distribution invites one to speculate that dopamine might have an important function in determining the distribution of cardiac output and maintenance of blood flow in vital organs.

Dopamine receptors are not confined to vascular smooth muscle; they exist in other smooth muscle tissues, in certain exocrine glands, and on the cell bodies and terminal varicosities of sympathetic nerves. The effects of dopamine which can be attributed to an action on a specific dopamine receptor are listed in Table 3.

**Table 3.** *Peripheral effects of dopamine attributable to actions on specific dopamine receptors [14]*

| Tissue or function | Effect |
|---|---|
| *Arterial smooth muscle* (isolated tissues) | |
| Renal | |
| Mesenteric | |
| Splenic | |
| Coronary | relaxation |
| Middle cerebral | |
| Pial | |
| Basilar | |
| Vertebral | |
| *Kidney* | |
| Sodium excretion | increase |
| *Gastrointestinal tract* | |
| Oesophageal tone | decrease |
| Intragastric pressure | decrease |
| Gastric emptying | delay |
| Intestinal motility | decrease |
| *Nervous structures* | |
| Transmitter release from sympathetic neurones | decrease |
| Ganglionic transmission in sympathetic ganglia | depression |
| Carotid chemoreceptor discharge | decrease |
| *Miscellaneous* | |
| Neurohypophyseal hormone release | stimulation |
| Exocrine pancreatic secretion | stimulation |
| Submandibular amylase secretion | stimulation |
| Platelet aggregation | stimulation |

## Sodium Excretion

The finding that dopamine-induced increases in renal blood flow are associated with increases in sodium excretion has been repeatedly documented in intact animals and man. Although this phenomenon was first reported in 1964, there is still controversy as to whether the natriuretic effect is due to a direct action of dopamine on tubular transport, or is secondary to an increase in total renal blood flow and glomerular filtration rate or to a redistribution of intrarenal blood flow [5, 23, 24].

An interesting aspect is that the amount of dopamine excreted in human urine is 5–20 times greater than that of noradrenaline or adrenaline. Initially the assumption was made that this reflected the filtered load of dopamine and was derived from the plasma. Now that more sensitive techniques for determining plasma catecholamines are available, it is clear that the amount of dopamine in the urine is far greater than can be accounted for by filtered plasma dopamine. Some workers have suggested that it might represent overspill from renal dopaminergic nerves. This seems unlikely in view of the rapid and effective re-uptake mechanisms present in sympathetic neurones, which are capable of conserving catecholamines when they are released into the synaptic cleft during nerve stimulation. A number of recent studies have led to the hypothesis that dopamine is generated within the kidney from circulating l-dopa [39]. It has been known for several years that the kidney is a very rich source of dopa-decarboxylase, and that this enzyme appears to be located principally in the proximal and distal tubules [27]. Inhibition of dopa-decarboxylase with carbidopa reduces not only the amount of dopamine in the urine, but also sodium excretion [3]. The depressant effect of carbidopa on sodium excretion is particularly marked following acute volume expansion [44].

These findings provide links in one of the most exciting aspects of the expanding research on dopamine, namely, the possibility that dopamine may have a physiological role in maintaining plasma volume by regulating renal sodium excretion [37]. Two interesting human studies initiated this hypothesis. The first showed that normal subjects on sodium restricted diets experienced a reduction in urinary dopamine and sodium excretion on assuming the upright position [16]. The second showed that a change from a low to a high sodium diet or infusion of saline increased dopamine excretion [1]; the response to saline infusion could not be accounted for by simple volume expansion [20]. These studies along with many others are very provocative, but none of the data obtained so far provides unequivocal proof that dopamine has a direct physiological effect on sodium excretion [24, 39]. Mills and his colleagues suggested, for example, that dopamine may activate a cascade of substances (e.g. the renal kallikrein-kinin-system, prostaglandins, and large and small molecular weight natriuretic peptides), all acting in concert to increase the kidney output of sodium [46, 47]. The relative importance of interactions between dopamine, renin, aldosterone and vasopressin remains to be assessed.

If it can be accepted that dopamine is an intrarenally-generated natriuretic substance, then it could be argued that a failure, or relative failure in its production might be an important factor in the genesis of some types of hypertension and oedema. The evidence at the moment is fragmentary, but such as there is appears to point in this direction [29, 39].

## Renin Secretion

The question as to whether renin secretion is under dopaminergic control remains unanswered, despite the impressive number of investigations which have been undertaken in isolated tissues, experimental animals and man [24]. In view of the complex actions of dopamine, this ambiguity is not surprising.

The vasodilator effects of dopamine resulting from actions on renal vascular receptors would tend to reduce renin activity, but this could well be offset by increases in renin activity mediated by simultaneous stimulation of $\beta$-adrenoceptors on cells in the juxtaglomerular apparatus; vasoconstriction resulting from $\alpha$-adrenoceptor or 5-HT receptor stimulation would have a similar effect. In the intact animal, the situation becomes even more complex since dopamine-induced changes in blood pressure, cardiac output and regional blood flow would all modify renin secretion indirectly.

In general, it appears that low doses of dopamine either do not alter or may depress renin secretion, whereas higher doses (which are usually associated with increases in blood pressure) enhance secretion. Increased secretion has been attributed to an action on a dopamine receptor only on the basis of antagonism of the effect with the dopamine blocking agent, haloperidol – but this compound has strong $\alpha$-adrenoceptor blocking activity, a fact which is often overlooked. There is, therefore, no convincing evidence as yet that renin secretion can be influenced directly via a dopamine receptor within the renal cortex [24].

## Effects on Ganglionic Transmission

The ability of dopamine to inhibit the function of the sympathetic nervous system has been recognized since 1963 [45]. Studies in the perfused hind limb of the dog, and cross circulation experiments clearly demonstrated inhibition of sympathetic transmission, but did not localize the site of action. Subsequently, it was shown that dilation only occurred when dopamine was allowed to reach the lumbar sympathetic ganglia [10].

Several early observations suggested that sympathetic ganglia are not merely simple relay stations. Histochemical techniques have demonstrated the presence of small chromaffin-type cells which exhibit an extremely bright fluorescence upon formaldehyde treatment. The substance responsible for the fluorescence in a variety of mammalian sympathetic ganglia is dopamine. These so-called small intensely fluorescent (SIF) cells are thought to be interneurones, which give rise to processes that impinge on the postganglionic cell body (Fig. 5). It has been proposed that dopamine, released by preganglionic muscarinic excitation of the SIF cells, acts on a receptor which in turn activates a specific adenylate cyclase in the postganglionic membrane. Accumulation of adenosine $3':5'$-monophosphate (cAMP) brings about transient hyperpolarization of the ganglion cell resulting in inhibition of transmission of impulses arising from the preganglionic neurone [18, 28, 40]. Much controversy has arisen with respect to the involvement of cAMP in the modulation of impulse transmission, and to the existence of a specific dopamine receptor in mammalian ganglia [13, 48]. Nevertheless, in vivo experiments show clearly that dopamine produces reversible inhibition of synaptic transmission in mesenteric and lumbar sympathetic ganglia of the dog [11, 41]. The receptor involved is indeed a dopamine receptor, which has been shown (by using appropriate agonists and antagonists) to resemble that in vascular smooth muscle [2, 42].

## Prejunctional Receptors

Inhibition of sympathetic neurotransmission by dopamine can also be demonstrated at a more distal site. It has been known for many years that noradrenaline and other $\alpha$-adrenoceptor agonists are capable of reducing the amount of tritiated noradrenaline released from postganglionic sympathetic nerves following nerve stimulation. The receptor responsible for this effect is believed to be located on or near nerve terminal varicosities (see Fig 6a). Although clearly an $\alpha$-adrenoceptor, it is not identical to that on the effector cell, since the relative potencies of various $\alpha$-adrenoceptor stimulants in inhibiting transmitter release and contracting smooth muscle are different. These findings formed the basis for the subdivision of $\alpha$-adrenoceptors into $\alpha_1$ (postjunctional) and $\alpha_2$ (prejunctional, i.e. neuronal).

Sympathetic nerve terminals are now believed to be endowed with many different receptors which are sensitive to transmitters released from adjacent nerve terminals, bloodborne compounds, or locally-formed substances. Compounds such as angiotensin, GABA, prostaglandins, opiates, adenosine, acetylcholine, $\beta$-adrenoceptor stimulants and dopamine can modulate sympathetic neurotransmission in many tissues by either enhancing or diminishing noradrenaline release [38].

The presence of dopamine receptors on sympathetic nerve terminals is now well established. In analogy to

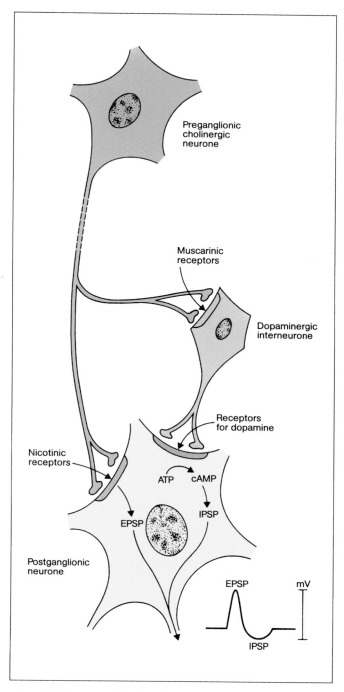

**Fig. 5.** *Possible mechanism of inhibitory modulation of ganglionic transmission by a dopaminergic interneurone. Impulses travelling in preganglionic fibres release acetylcholine from the synaptic terminals. Acetylcholine stimulates the ganglion cell by acting on nicotinic receptors, and also stimulates the dopaminergic interneurone via muscarinic receptors. Stimulation of the interneurone results in the release of dopamine which, by acting on specific receptors on the postganglionic neurone, triggers the formation of cAMP. This gives rise to an inhibitory postsynaptic potential (IPSP) which modulates or attenuates the excitatory action potential (EPSP) produced by the nicotinic action of acetylcholine*

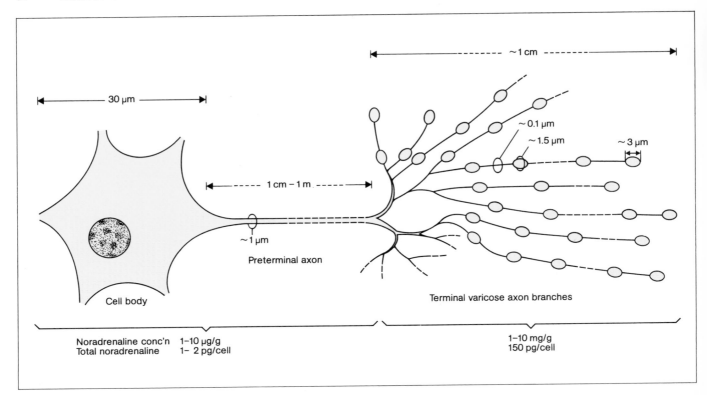

**Fig. 6 a.** *Diagram of an adrenergic neurone showing dimensions and concentrations of noradrenaline within it. The only portion of a post-ganglionic autonomic neurone that can be identified by light microscopy is the cell body. Fluorescent histochemistry and electron microscopy have revealed that noradrenaline-containing adrenergic neurones appear as* *beaded strands which form a network in and around groups of effector cells. The beaded structure of the terminal axons is due to the presence, at intervals of 3–10 μm, of swellings 1–2 μm in diameter. The swellings, or varicosities, are thought to be the actual sites of transmitter release, and constitute **en passant** junctions rather than terminal junctions.*

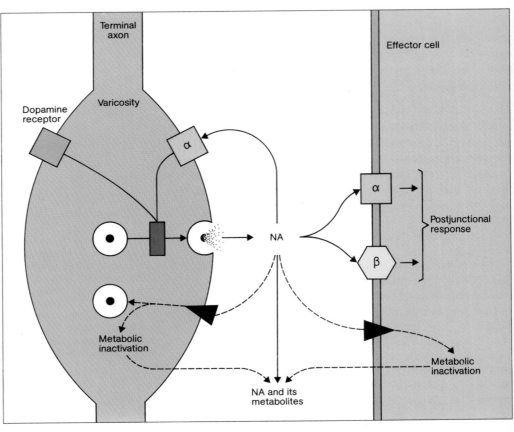

**Fig. 6 b.** *Diagram of a noradrenergic junction showing a varicosity of a terminal noradrenergic axon on the left and an effector cell on the right. Noradrenaline (NA) is released from granular storage vesicles by exocytosis in response to nerve impulses, and acts postjunctionally on α- or β-adrenoceptors. Its stimulant effects are terminated rapidly by neuronal and extraneuronal uptake followed by metabolic degradation or re-incorporation into nerve storage vesicles. The amount of noradrenaline released is thought to be limited by the transmitter itself via stimulation of α-adrenoceptors situated on or near the terminal axon. Prejunctional dopamine receptors mediate a similar effect; although their physiological significance is not yet established, they nevertheless constitute a possible site of action for potential antihypertensive agents*

noradrenaline, dopamine depresses stimulation-evoked noradrenaline release and the response of the effector cell (Fig. 6b). Its action is unaffected by phentolamine, but is reversed by dopamine receptor antagonists [32].

Structure-activity relationship studies with a variety of dopamine analogues and related compounds have shown that the rank orders of potency in stimulating prejunctional and postjunctional (vascular) receptors are not the same. Many potent prejunctional receptor stimulants have negligible effects on postjunctional receptors, and a few compounds have been discovered for which the reverse is true [25]. The chemical structures of the most selective pre- and postjunctional dopamine receptor stimulants are depicted in Fig. 7. Experiments using antagonists are limited, but

more convincing in differentiating the two receptor subtypes. Haloperidol, butaclamol and bulbocapnine are relatively non-selective, but domperidone and the S-enantiomer of sulpiride are at least 500 times more potent in blocking the prejunctional than the postjunctional receptor. The recent discovery of a compound (SCH 23390) which is a potent antagonist of the vascular effects of dopamine but has no inhibitory effect at the prejunctional receptor completes the evidence required for classifying peripheral dopamine receptors into two subgroups [25]. The postjunctional receptor is designated $DA_1$, and the prejunctional $DA_2$. Whether these receptors correspond to the $D_1$ and $D_2$ receptors described in the central nervous system remains to be established, but on the basis of available evidence it seems that they are not identical.

Effects on prejunctional receptors on nerves innervating blood vessels make an important contribution to the hypotensive and vasodilator effects of dopamine, particularly when sympathetic tone is high. Figure 8 illustrates experiments which show that when the major vascular beds containing postjunctional dopamine receptors are eliminated from the circulation (by ligating the renal and splanchnic vessels), injections of dopamine can still produce substantial falls in blood pressure and these can be abolished by suppressing neuronal activity with a ganglion blocker [15].

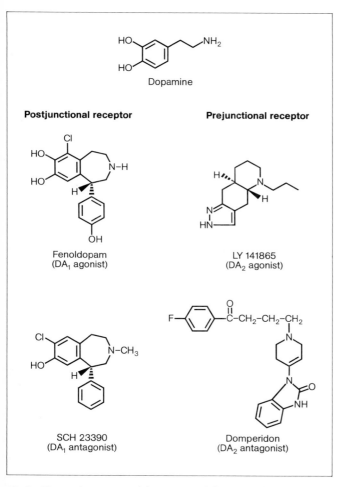

*Fig. 7. Chemical structures of dopamine and the most selective postjunctional ($DA_1$) and prejunctional ($DA_2$) dopamine receptor agonists and antagonists. Structure-activity relationship studies have shown that a $DA_1$ receptor stimulant must possess 2 hydroxyl groups (analogous to the 3,4-OH of dopamine), separated from the nitrogen atom by a distance of 7-8 angstrom units. Note the similarity between the structures of the selective $DA_1$ agonist fenoldopam and the antagonist SCH 23390. The structural requirements for combining with $DA_2$ receptors are far less strict. Members of a variety of structure classes stimulate the receptor, e.g. dopamine, apomorphine and ergoline derivatives, ergot alkaloids, and aminotetralines; antagonists include phenothiazines, butyrophenones and substituted benzamides*

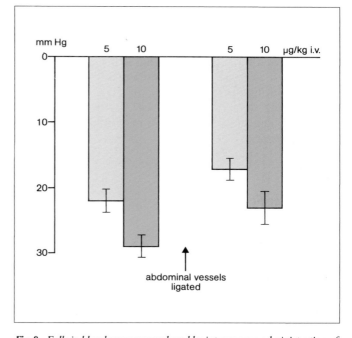

*Fig. 8. Falls in blood pressure produced by intravenous administration of dopamine in dogs anaesthetized with chloralose and urethane. This anaesthesia produces a high sympathetic tone, and the initial pressor response to dopamine seen under barbiturate anaesthesia is absent. Exclusion of the major vascular beds possessing dopamine receptors from the circulation results in only small reductions in the responses to dopamine injections. The residual effects are not significantly affected by blockade of β-adrenoceptors, but are abolished by ganglion blockade. n = 16*

Compounds which exert a selective effect on prejunctional dopamine receptors are very effective hypotensive agents. The prolactin secretion inhibitor bromocriptine (Parlodel), for instance, produces marked blood pressure falls in experimental animals, which are proportional to the pre-existing sympathetic tone. The hypothesis that the cardiovascular effects of bromocriptine are due to a decrease in noradrenaline efflux is supported by observations that following oral administration to healthy subjects and hypertensive patients, plasma levels of noradrenaline decrease significantly both at rest and during exercise [14].

An important feature of compounds acting on prejunctional dopamine receptors is that the reductions in blood pressure which they produce are not associated with reflex increases in heart rate; heart rate either does not change or may decrease, Reflex tachycardia is prevented by inhibition of noradrenaline release from the accelerans nerve. A further observation made in dogs is that even when heart rate is reduced, there is not always a corresponding decline in myocardial contractile force (Fig. 9). In this species there seems to be a differential distribution of prejunctional receptors in nerves innervating the heart; they are clearly present in nerves innervating the sinus node but are absent in nerves controlling ventricular contractility [14].

Prejunctional dopamine receptors are also lacking in other noradrenergic nerves, such as those innervating the guinea pig vas deferens, rabbit and rat heart, guinea pig atrium and cat hindquarters. Indeed, Gillespie regarded the failure of dopamine to inhibit release in some tissues in which an excellent prejunctional $\alpha$-mediated inhibition can be shown as supportive evidence favouring the existence of prejunctional dopamine receptors [22]. If these receptors have a functional role, what is the source of dopamine? Is it released with noradrenaline from the nerve terminal during stimulation [31], or is it derived from neighbouring dopaminergic nerves? There is a growing body of evidence that such nerves may indeed be present in the periphery.

## Dopaminergic Nerves

The impetus which liberated dopamine from its solely precursor role came during the 1960s when it was found that in some neurones of vertebrate and invertebrate brains, dopamine existed without the concomitant presence of noradrenaline [34, 36, 51]. Dopamine-$\beta$-hydroxylase, the enzyme necessary for the conversion of dopamine to noradrenaline, is lacking in these neruones so that dopamine is the end-product of synthesis and acts as a transmitter in its own right. This fundamental finding coincided with the discovery of dopamine receptors in vascular smooth muscle. The stage was set for examining the possibility that a population of dopaminergic nerves might also exist in the autonomic nervous system, since a specific receptor is a self-evident prerequisite for a substance to act as a transmitter of neural impulses.

Several criteria have to be met, however, before one can assume that a naturally occurring substance is a transmitter. High concentrations of the putative transmitter, and the enzymes necessary for its synthesis must be present in the neurone. Electrical stimulation of the nerve should release sufficient amounts of the substance in question to produce the appropriate effect on the end-organ, and the effector response should be abolished by pharmacological agents thought to bind selectively to specific receptor types.

Electrical stimulation of sympathetic nerves innervating blood vessels produces only vasoconstriction, due to noradrenaline release. This can be prevented by pretreating animals with guanethidine (vide infra) or phenoxybenzamine. In the kidney (rat, dog), mesenteric vasculature (dog) and vessels of the paw pad (dog) a vasodilator response is unmasked, which is abolished selectively by dopamine-receptor blocking agents. Antagonists of dopamine have also been found to depress receptive relaxation in the stomach, and enhance reflex oesephageal contraction due to local distension. Such findings are strongly suggestive of a dopaminergic innervation to these regions [4].

The presence of dopaminergic nerves in the central nervous system was established largely using histochemical and biochemical techniques. The obvious similarities between dopaminergic and noradrenergic neurones did not prove a barrier in establishing their independent existence because their cell bodies and axon fields are anatomically distinct. The situation in the periphery, however, is far more complex since sympathetic neurones are ubiquitous, and all nerve bundles are likely to be mixed. In addition, direct demonstration of dopamine-containing nerves is technically difficult because the amine is present in all sympathetic nerves as a precursor of noradrenaline.

A useful technique by which dopaminergic neurones can be visualized histochemically is to deplete tissues of noradrenaline stores with guanethidine. The noradrenergic neurone blocking activity of this drug is brought about by uptake into the axon and displacement of noradrenaline from storage vesicles. One or other of these processes appears to be less efficient in brain neurones which are thought to be dopaminergic, i.e. doses of guanethidine which affect fluorescence in noradrenergic neurones are without effect on the dopaminergic population [19, 21]. This technique has proved useful for selectively visualizing dopaminergic neurones and measuring dopamine levels in the periphery also.

Guanethidine treatment causes a pronounced reduction in tissue levels of both noradrenaline and dopamine together with abolition of visible catecholamine fluorescence in the atrium and vas deferens of the dog; these are tissues for which there is no evidence for a dopaminergic innervation. By contrast, the dopamine content in the renal cortex and paw pads is virtually unaffected, and some axons around the juxtaglomerular arterioles and pedal arteriovenous shunts retain strong fluorescence [7, 8]. Other

**Fig. 9.** *Mean reductions ($\pm$ SE) in heart rate and myocardial contractile force in the anaesthetised dog produced by a prejunctional dopamine receptor stimulant (bromocriptine), a β-adrenoceptor blocking agent (propranolol), and a prejunctional α-adrenoceptor stimulant (guanfacine). Contractile force was measured by means of a strain gauge arch sewn onto the surface of the right ventricle. The doses selected for each compound reduced heart rate by approximately 20 beats/min. Note that the changes in contractility produced by propranolol and guanfacine are much greater than that produced by bromocriptine. (Doses of bromocriptine and guanfacine were infused over 10 and 40 min respectively (horizontal bars); propranolol was administered as a single bolus injection [14]*

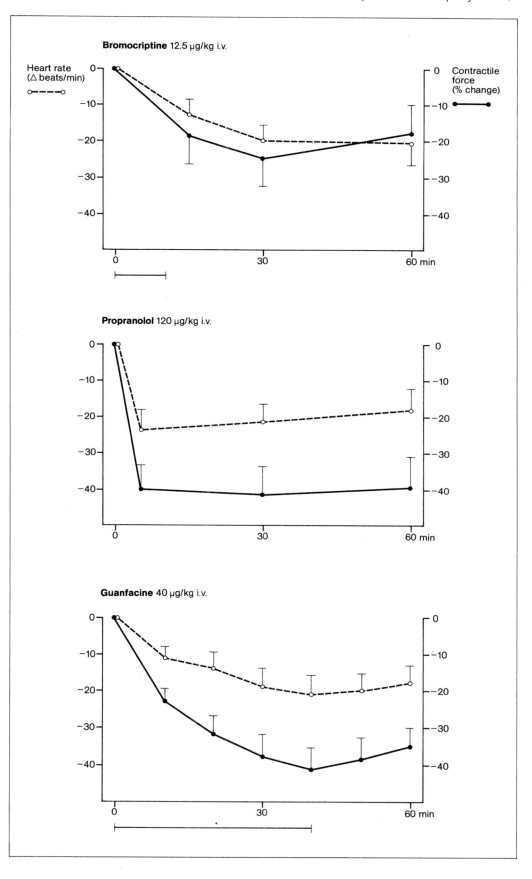

**Table 4.** *Comparative properties of "typical" postganglionic noradrenergic neurones and putative dopaminergic neurones [4]*

|  | Noradrenergic | Dopaminergic |
|---|---|---|
| Transmitter release | Reserpine sensitive<br>Guanethidine sensitive | Reserpine sensitive<br>Guanethidine resistant |
| Transmitter action | Not affected by DA antagonists | Attenuated by DA antagonists<br>Prolonged by the DA-uptake inhibitor benztropine |
| Amine levels | DA:NA constant and low<br>Guanethidine depletes DA and NA<br>6-OH DA depletes DA and NA<br>Reserpine depletes DA and NA | DA high<br><br>Guanethidine does not affect DA<br>6-OH DA depletes DA<br>Reserpine depletes DA |
| Amine synthesis | L-DOPA only slowly processed after reserpine depletion of amines; no vesicle reloading<br>High DBH content | L-DOPA rapidly decarboxylated and vesicles reloaded<br><br><br>Low (no?) DBH content |

DA, dopamine;    NA, noradrenaline;    DBH, dopamine β-hydroxylase

techniques have shown that the concentration of dopamine is up to five times that expected from the segmental noradrenaline content in prevertebral and paravertebral ganglia of the sympathetic chain which supply axons to the kidney and hindpaw. Relatively high dopamine levels, compared with those of noradrenaline, are also present in the coeliac, superior mesenteric and renal ganglia [6]. Table 4 summarizes some of the biochemical and pharmacological properties of putative dopaminergic neurones which differentiate them from typical postganglionic noradrenergic neurones.

Dinerstein and his colleagues demonstrated elegantly with the aid of a microspectrophotometric technique that neurones innervating larger arterioles and arteries in the dog kidney contain predominantly noradrenaline, whereas the neuronal elements at the glomerular vascular poles throughout the cortex contain predominantly dopamine. The location of these dopamine-containing elements places them contiguous not only with vessels that can regulate blood flow through the glomeruli, but also with the juxtamedullary apparatus. If dopamine is released from these stores as the result of physiological stimuli, a dopaminergic component in the normal regulation of renal blood flow and renin release may exist [17].

Some of the evidence presented in support of a peripheral neurotransmitter role for dopamine is circumstantial (which is not unusual in neuroscience), and the morphological data is limited. There is, however, sufficient experimental data to propose that dopamine serves an independent role in peripheral neurotransmission. Whether dopamine occurs independently in specific neurones, or is a cotransmitter in sympathetic neurones still remains to be investigated.

## Conclusion

Although the physiological role of dopamine receptors in the periphery remains to be established, there is no doubt as to their pharmacological importance. Their anatomical distribution within the cardiovascular system, kidney and sympathetic nervous system is such that a long-acting, selective agonist might be expected to produce therapeutically useful effects. A compound which would dilate the more vital vascular beds (mesenteric, renal, coronary and cerebral), prevent neuronally-mediated increases in blood pressure and heart rate, reduce circulating noradrenaline and increase sodium excretion has the features of a desirable antihypertensive agent, and may well be of benefit in treating congestive cardiac failure and renal failure. In addition, the development of selective agonists and antagonists as pharmacological tools will increase our knowledge concerning the location of dopamine receptors and their physiological importance. This in turn may open up fresh avenues for the development of new medicines.

## References

1. Alexander RW, Gill JR, Yamabe H, Lovenberg W, Keiser HR (1974) Effects of dietary sodium and of acute saline infusion on the inter-relationship between dopamine excretion and adrenergic activity in man. J Clin Invest 54: 194–200
2. Alkadhi KA, Sabouni MH, Lokhandwala MF (to be published) Characterisation of ganglionic dopamine receptors in spontaneously hypertensive (SHR) and normotensive rats. 9th International Congress on Pharmacology, London, 1984
3. Ball SG, Lee MR (1977) The effect of Carbidopa administration on urinary sodium excretion in man. Is dopamine an intrarenal natriuretic hormone? Br J Clin Pharmacol 4: 115–119
4. Bell C (1982) Dopamine as a postganglionic autonomic neurotransmitter. Neuroscience 7: 1–8
5. Bell C, Lang WJ (1982) Is there a place for dopamine in autonomic neuromuscular transmission? In: Kalsner S (ed) Autonomic pharmacology, vol 2. Urban and Schwarzenberg, Munich, pp 263–282
6. Bell C, McLachlan EM (1982) Dopaminergic neurons in sympathetic ganglia of the dog. Proc R Soc Lond [Biol] 215: 175–190
7. Bell C, Lang WJ, Laska F (1978). Dopamine-containing vasomotor nerves in the dog kidney. J Neurochem 31: 77–83
8. Bell C, Lang WJ, Laska F (1978) Dopamine-containing axons supplying the arterio-venous anastomoses of the canine paw pad. J Neurochem 31: 1329–1333
9. Blaschko H (1957) Metabolism and storage of biogenic amines. Experientia 13: 9–12
10. Bogaert MG, de Schaepdryver AF (1967) Dopamine-induced neurogenic vasodilation in the hindleg of the dog. Arch Int Pharmacodyn Ther 166: 203–207
11. Bogaert MG, de Schaepdryver AF, Willems JL (1977) Dopamine-induced neurogenic vasodilation in the intact hindleg of the dog. Br J Pharmacol 59: 283–292

12. Brodde OE (1982) Vascular dopamine receptors: demonstration and characterisation by in vitro studies. Life Sci 31: 289–306

13. Brown DA, Caulfield M (1978) Adrenoceptors in sympathetic ganglia. In: Szabadi E, Bradshaw CM, Bevan P (eds) Recent advances in the pharmacology of adrenoceptors. Elsevier/North-Holland Biomedical, Amsterdam, pp 57–66

14. Clark BJ (1981) Dopamine receptors and the cardiovascular system. Postgrad Med J [Suppl 1] 57: 45–54

15. Clark BJ, Menninger K (1980) Peripheral dopamine receptors. Circ Res 46: I-59–I-63

16. Cuche JL, Kuchel O, Barbeau A, Boucher R, Genest J (1972) Relationship between the adrenergic nervous system and renin during adaptation to upright posture: a possible role for 3,4-dihydroxyphenethylamine (dopamine). Clin Sci 43: 481–489

17. Dinerstein RJ, Vannice J, Henderson RC, Roth LJ, Goldberg LI, Hoffmann PC (1979) Histofluorescent techniques provide evidence for dopamine-containing neuronal elements in canine kidney. Science 205: 497–499

18. Eränkö O (1978) Small intensely fluorescent (SIF) cells and nervous transmission in sympathetic ganglia. Annu Rev Pharmacol Toxicol 18: 417–430

19. Evans BK, Singer G, Armstrong S, Saunders PE, Burnstock G (1975) Effects of chronic intracranial injection of low and high concentrations of guanethidine in the rat. Pharmacol Biochem Behav 3: 219–228

20. Faucheux B, Buu NT, Kuchel O (1977) Effects of saline and albumin on plasma and urinary catecholamines in dogs. Am J Physiol 232: F123–F127

21. Fuxe K, Hamberger B, Malmfors T (1967) The effects of drugs on accumulation of monoamines in tuberoinfundibular neurons. Eur J Pharmacol 1: 334–341

22. Gillespie JS (1980) Presynaptic receptors in the autonomic nervous system. In: Szekeres L (ed) Adrenergic activators and inhibitors. Springer, Berlin Heidelberg New York, pp 353–425 (Handbook of experimental pharmacology, vol 54/1)

23. Goldberg LI (1972) Cardiovascular and renal actions of dopamine: potential clinical applications. Pharmacol Rev 24: 1–29

24. Goldberg LI, Weder AB (1980) Connections between endogenous dopamine, dopamine receptors and sodium excretion: evidences and hypotheses. In: Turner P, Shand D (eds) Recent advances in clinical pharmacology, vol 2. Livingstone, Edinburgh, pp 149–166

25. Goldberg LI, Kohli JD, Glock D (1984) Complete separation of peripheral DA, and DA₂ receptors by selective antagonists. Clin Neuropharmacol [Suppl 1] 7: 802–803

26. Goldberg LI, McDonald RH, Zimmermann AM (1963) Sodium diureses produced by dopamine in patients with congestive heart failure. N Engl J Med 208: 1060–1064

27. Goldstein M, Fuxe K, Hökfelt T (1972) Characterisation and tissue localisation of catecholamine synthesising enzymes. Pharmacol Rev 24: 293–308

28. Greengard P, Kebabian JW (1974) Role of cyclic AMP in synaptic transmission in the mammalian peripheral nervous system. Fed Proc 33: 1059–1067

29. Harvey JN, Casson IF, Clayden AD, Cope GF, Perkins CM, Lee MR (1984) A paradoxical fall in urine dopamine output when patients with essential hypotension are given added dietary salt. Clin Sci 67: 83–88

30. Holz P, Credner K (1942) Die enzymatische Entstehung von Oxytyramin im Organismus und die physiologische Bedeutung der Dopadecarboxylase. Naunyn Schmiedebergs Arch Exp Pathol Pharmakol 200: 356–388

31. Hope W, Majewski H, McCulloch MW, Rand MJ, Story DF (1980) Evidence for a modulatory role of dopamine in sympathetic transmission. Circ Res [Suppl 1] 46: I-77–I-79

32. Hope W, McCulloch MW, Rand MJ, Story DF (1978) Modulation of noradrenergic transmission in the rabbit ear artery by dopamine. Br J Pharmacol 64: 527–537

33. Hornykiewicz O (1971) Dopamine: its physiology, pharmacology and pathological neurochemistry. In: Biel JH, Abood LG (eds) Biogenic amines and physiological membranes in drug therapy. Dekker, New York, pp 173–258 (Medicinal research series, part B)

34. Hornykiewicz O (1973) Dopamine in the basal ganglia: its role and therapeutic implications (including the clinical use of L-dopa). Br Med Bull 29: 172–178

35. Horwitz D, Fox SM, Goldberg LI (1962) Effects of dopamine in man. Circ Res 10: 237–243

36. Kerkut GA (1973) Catecholamines in invertebrates. Br Med Bull 29: 100–104

37. Kuchel O, Buu NT, Unger T (1978) Dopamine-sodium relationship: is dopamine a part of the endogenous natriuretic system? Contrib Nephrol 13: 27–36

38. Langer SZ, Arbilla S (1981) Presynaptic receptors and modulation of the release of noradrenaline, dopamine and GABA. Postgrad Med J [Suppl 1] 57: 18–29

39. Lee MR (1982) Dopamine and the kidney. Clin Sci 62: 439–448

40. Libet B (1979) Which postsynaptic action of dopamine is mediated by cyclic AMP? Life Sci 24: 1043–1058

41. Lins RL, Willems JL (1974) Dopamine-induced inhibition of synaptic transmission in the inferior mesenteric ganglion of the dog. Arch Int Pharmacodyn 208: 367–368

42. Lokhandwala MF, Watkins H, Alkadhi KA (to be published) Pharmacological analysis of the action of SKF 82526 on cardiovascular dopamine receptors (Abstr) 9th International Congress on Pharmacology, London, 1984

43. MacCannell KL, McNay JL, Meyer MB, Goldberg LI (1966) Dopamine in the treatment of hypotension and shock. N Engl J Med 275: 1389–1398

44. McClanahan M, Sowers JR, Beck FWJ, Mohanty PK (1983) Dopaminergic regulation of natriuretic response to acute volume expansion. Clin Res 31: 835A

45. McDonald RH, Goldberg LI (1963) Analysis of the cardiovascular effects of dopamine in the dog. J Pharmacol Exp Ther 140: 60–66

46. Mills I, Obika L (1975) The effect of adrenergic and dopamine receptor blockade on the kallikrein and renal response to intraarterial infusion of dopamine in dogs. J Physiol 263: 150P

47. Mills I, Newport P, Obika L (1981) Kallikrein and kinins in the control of blood pressure. In: Blaufox MD, Bianchi C (eds) Secondary forms of hypertension. Grune and Stratton, New York, pp 195–203

48. Quenzer L, Yahn D, Alkadhi K, Volle RL (1979) Transmission blockade and stimulation of ganglionic adenylate cyclase by catecholamines. J Pharmacol Exp Ther 208: 31–36

49. Rajfer SI, Anton AH, Rossen JD, Goldberg LI (1984) Beneficial hemodynamic effects of oral levodopa in heart failure. N Engl J Med 310: 1357–1362

50. Schmidt M, Imbs JL (1980) Pharmacological characterisation of renal vascular dopamine receptors. J Cardiovasc Pharmacol 2: 595–605

51. Vogt M (1973) Functional aspects of the role of catecholamines in the central nervous system. Br Med Bull 29: 168–172